COGAT® TEST PREP
GIFTED AND TALENTED TEST PREPARATION
Level 10

Gateway Gifted Resources™
www.GatewayGifted.com

PLEASE LEAVE
US A REVIEW!

Thank you for selecting this book. We are a family-owned publishing company - a consortium of educators, test designers, book designers, parents, and kid-testers.

We would be thrilled if you left us a quick review on the website where you purchased this book!

The Gateway Gifted Resources™ Team
www.GatewayGifted.com

TABLE OF CONTENTS

INTRODUCTION

- About This Book & About The COGAT® 4
- Test-Taking Tips 5
- 'We Need Your Help' / Points Tracking 5
- Question Examples & Explanations 6

PRACTICE TEST 1 (WORKBOOK FORMAT)

- Verbal Classification 10
- Verbal Analogies 13
- Sentence Completion 16
- Figure Classification 21
- Figure Analogies 29
- Paper Folding Puzzles 37
- Number Puzzles 43
- Number Analogies 47
- Number Series 52

PRACTICE TEST 2

- Verbal Classification 57
- Verbal Analogies 59
- Sentence Completion 61
- Figure Classification 65
- Figure Analogies 72
- Paper Folding Puzzles 79
- Number Puzzles 84
- Number Analogies 88
- Number Series 92

ANSWER KEY FOR PRACTICE TEST 1 (WORKBOOK FORMAT) 96

ANSWER KEY FOR PRACTICE TEST 2 98

BUBBLE SHEET FOR PRACTICE TEST 2 101

ADDITIONAL BOOKS 102

ABOUT THIS BOOK: This book helps prepare children for the COGAT® Level 10, a test given to fourth graders. Not only will this publication help prepare children for the COGAT®, these logic-based exercises may also be used for other gifted test preparation and as critical thinking exercises. This book has five parts.

1. Introduction (p.4-9): About this book & the COGAT®, Test Taking Tips, Points Tracking, and Question Examples

2. Practice Test 1 (Workbook Format) (p.10-56): These pages are designed similarly to content tested in the COGAT®'s nine test question types. Unless your child already has experience with COGAT® prep materials, you should complete Practice Test 1 (Workbook Format) together with no time limit. **Before doing this section with your child, read the Question Examples & Explanations (p.6-9).**

3. Practice Test 2 (p.57-95): Practice Test 2 helps children develop critical thinking and test-taking skills. It provides an introduction to standardized testing in a relaxed manner (parents provide guidance if needed) and an opportunity for children to focus on a group of questions for a longer time period (something to which some children are not accustomed). This part is also a way for parents to identify points of strength/ weakness in COGAT® question types. Practice Test 2 is divided into three sections to mirror the three COGAT® batteries: Verbal, Quantitative, and Non-Verbal.

4. Answer Keys (p.96-100): These pages contain the Practice Test answers as well as brief answer explanations.

5. Bubble Sheet for Practice Test 2 (p.101-102)

ABOUT THE COGAT® LEVEL 10: The COGAT® (Cognitive Abilities Test®) test is divided into 3 "batteries."
- *Verbal Battery; total time: around 45 minutes*
Question Types (15 minutes each, approximately): Verbal Analogies, Verbal Classification, Sentence Completion
- *Non-Verbal Battery; total time: around 45 minutes*
Question Types (15 minutes each, approximately): Figure Analogies, Figure Classification, Paper Folding
- *Quantitative Battery; total time: around 45 minutes*
Question Types (15 minutes each, approximately): Number Series, Number Puzzles, Number Analogies

The test has 176 questions total. The test, about two hours in length, is administered in different testing sessions. Children are not expected to finish 176 questions in one session. **See pages 6 to 9 for details on question types.**

ABOUT COGAT® TESTING PROCEDURES: These vary by school. Tests may be given individually or in a group. These tests may be used as the single factor for admission to gifted programs, or they may be used in combination with IQ tests or as part of a student "portfolio." They are used by some schools together with tests like Iowa Assessments™. Check with your testing site to determine its specific testing procedures.

QUESTION NOTE: Because each child has different cognitive abilities, the questions in this book are at varied skill levels. The exercises may or may not require a great deal of parental guidance to complete, depending on your child's abilities, prior test prep experience, or prior testing experience. Most sections of the Workbook begin with a relatively easy question. We suggest always completing at least the first question together, ensuring your child is not confused about what the question asks or with the directions.

"BUBBLES" NOTE: Your child will most likely have to fill in "bubbles" (the circles) to indicate answer choices. Show your child how to fill in the bubble to indicate his/her answer choice using a pencil. If your child needs to change his/her answer, (s)he should erase the original mark and fill in the new choice.

SCORING NOTE: Check with your school/program for its scoring procedure and admissions requirements. Here is a general summary of the COGAT® scoring process. First, your child's raw score is established. This is the number of questions correctly answered. Points are not deducted for questions answered incorrectly. Next, this score is compared to other test-takers of his/her same age group (and, for the COGAT®, the same grade level) using various indices to then calculate your child's stanine (a score from one to nine) and percentile rank. If your child achieved the percentile rank of 98%, then (s)he scored as well as or better than 98% of test-takers. In general, gifted programs accept scores of *at least* 98% or *higher*. Please note that a percentile rank "score" cannot be obtained from our practice material. This material has not been given to a large enough sample of test-takers to develop any kind of base score necessary for percentile rank calculations.

TEST TAKING TIPS

• **Be sure your child looks carefully at each answer choice.** COGAT® questions can be quite challenging. Even if your child thinks (s)he knows the answer - (s)he should look at each choice.

• **Have your child practice listening carefully.** Paying attention is important - test questions are not repeated.

• **Test-takers receive points for the number of correct answers.** If your child says that (s)he does not know the answer, (s)he should eliminate any answers that are clearly incorrect. Guess instead of leaving a question blank.

• **In the Workbook section, go through the exercises together by talking about them:** what the exercise is asking the child to do and what makes the answer choices correct/incorrect. This will familiarize your child with working through exercises and will help to develop a process of elimination (getting rid of incorrect answer choices).

• **Remember common sense tips like getting enough sleep.** It has been scientifically proven that kids perform below their grade level when tired. **Feed them a breakfast for sustained energy and concentration** (complex carbohydrates and protein; avoid foods/drinks high in sugar). Have them use the restroom prior to the test.

POINTS TRACKING

To increase child engagement and to add an incentive to complete book exercises, a game theme accompanies this book. As your child completes the Practice Tests, (s)he earns 1 point per question.

Some parents may want to offer a special treat as well for completion, although this is at the parent's discretion.

WE NEED YOUR HELP! *(For kids and parents to read together.)*

We've got a challenge for you! Are you up for it?

This book is filled with mind-bending, challenging questions, and we need your help to answer them.

For every question you answer, you earn 1 point.

So far, the highest score anyone has ever earned is 374 points. Do you have what it takes to earn 374? Use the space below to track your points.

The questions start on page 10. Your parent (or other adult) will let you know what you need to do. Remember to:

• try to answer the questions the right way (instead of trying to finish really fast)
• pay attention
• look closely at all choices before choosing an answer
• keep trying even if some questions are hard

Alex May Sophie Anya Freddie Max

CAN YOU EARN 374 POINTS?

POINTS TRACKING

Date	Points	Date	Points	Date	Points
_____	_____	_____	_____	_____	_____
_____	_____	_____	_____	_____	_____

QUESTION EXAMPLES & EXPLANATIONS   This section introduces the nine COGAT® question types with simple examples/explanations. Questions in Practice Test 1 & 2 will be more challenging than those below.

VERBAL BATTERY

1. VERBAL ANALOGIES   Directions: Look at the first set of words. Try to figure out how they belong together. Next, look at the second set of words. The answer is missing. Figure out which answer choice would make the second set go together in the same way that the first set goes together.

toe > foot : petal > ?   stem   bee   leg   flower   colorful

Explanation   Here are some strategies to help your child select the correct answer:
• Try to come up with a "rule" describing how the first set goes together. Take this rule, apply it to the first word in the second set. Determine which answer choice makes the second set follow the same "rule." If more than one choice works, you need a more specific rule. Here, a "rule" for the first set is that "the first word (toe) is part of the second word (foot)." In the next set, using this rule, "flower" is the answer. A petal is part of a flower.
• Another strategy is to come up with a sentence describing how the first set of words go together. A sentence would be: A toe is part of a foot. Then, take this sentence and apply it to the word in the second set: A petal is part of a ?. Figure out which answer choice would best complete the sentence. (It would be "flower.")
• Ensure your child does not choose a word simply because it *has to do with* the first set. For example, choice A ("stem") *has to do with* a petal, but does not follow the rule.

The simple examples will introduce your child to analogical thinking. Read the "Question" then "Answer Choices" to your child. Which choice goes best? (The answer is underlined.)

Analogy Logic	Question	Answer Choices (Answer is Underlined)			
• Antonyms	On *is to* Off -as- Hot *is to* ?	Warm	Sun	Cold	Oven
• Synonyms	Big *is to* Large -as- Horrible *is to* ?	Tired	Stale	Sour	Awful
• Whole: Part	Tree *is to* Branch -as- House *is to* ?	Street	Apartment	Room	Home
• Degree	Good *is to* Excellent -as- Tired *is to* ?	Boring	Exhausted	Drowsy	Slow
• Object: Location	Sun *is to* Sky -as- Swing *is to* ?	Playground	Monkey Bars	Sidewalk	Grass
• Same Animal Class	Turkey *is to* Parrot -as- Ant *is to* ?	Worm	Beetle	Duck	Spider
• Object: Creator	Painting *is to* Artist -as- Furniture *is to* ?	Carpenter	Tool	Chair	Potter
• Object: Container	Ice Cube *is to* Ice Tray -as- Flower *is to* ?	Petal	Vase	Smell	Florist
• Tool: Worker	Paintbrush *is to* Artist -as- Microscope *is to* ?	Telescope	Scientist	Lab	Fireman
• Object: 3D Shape	Ball *is to* Sphere -as- Dice *is to* ?	Line	Square	Cone	Cube
• Object: Location Used	Jet *is to* Sky -as- Canoe *is to* ?	Boat	Paddle	Water	Sail
• Object: Location Used	Chalk *is to* Chalkboard -as- Paintbrush *is to* ?	Artist	Easel	Paint	Eraser

2. VERBAL CLASSIFICATION   Directions: Look at the three words on the top row. Figure out how the words are alike. Next, look at the words in the answer choices. Which word goes best with the three words in the top row?

cake   bread   muffin

A. bakery   B. sherbet   C. cookie   D. syrup   E. sugar

Explanation   Come up with a "rule" describing how they're alike. Then, see which answer choice follows the rule. If more than one choice does, you need a more specific rule.
• At first, test-takers may say the rule for the top words is that "they are all a kind of food." However, more than one answer choice would fit this rule. A more specific rule is needed. A more specific rule would be that "the foods are baked foods." Therefore, the best answer is "cookie."
• Ensure your child does not choose a word simply because it has to do with the top three. For example, choice A (bakery) has to do with the three, as all three could be found at a bakery. However, "bakery" is not a baked food. Another simple example:

fall   spring   summer

A. warm   B. season   C. month   D. winter   E. weather

This example demonstrates a common mistake. Note answer choice "B", season. Here, the question logic (or, rule) is "seasons." A child, having the rule "seasons" in their mind, may mistakenly choose "season." However, the answer is "winter," because "winter," like the top three words, is an *example* of a season.

Below are additional simple examples to introduce your child to classification logic.

- function and uses of common objects (i.e., writing and drawing / measuring / cutting / drinking / eating)

Fork / Chopsticks / Knife   Choices: Stove / Straw / Meat / <u>Spoon</u>   (Used For Eating)

- location of common objects

Refrigerator / Cabinet / Table   Choices: Bed / Restaurant / <u>Oven</u> / Shower   (Found In Kitchens)

- appearance of common objects (i.e., color; objects in pairs; objects with stripes vs. spots; object's shape)

Ketchup / Blood / Firetruck   Choices: <u>Cherry</u> / Mustard / Cucumber / Police car   (Red)

- characteristics of common objects (i.e., hot, cold)

Ice / Igloo / Popsicle   Choices: Cookie / <u>Snowman</u> / Palm Tree / Coffee   (Cold)

- animal types

Leopard / Cheetah / Kitten   Choices: Elephant / Giraffe/ <u>Tiger</u> / Bat   (Cats)

- natural habitats

Swamp / River / Pond   Choices: Desert / Mountain / House / <u>Ocean</u>   (Water)

- food growing location (i.e., on a tree, under the ground as a root, or on a vine)

Potato / Carrot / Onion   Choices: <u>Radish</u> / Melon / Pepper / Broccoli   (Root Vegetables)

- professions, community helpers

Doctor / Fireman / Vet   Choices: Witch / Wizard / <u>Teacher</u> / Baby   (Community Helpers)

- clothing (i.e., in what weather it's worn; on what body part it's worn)

Crown / Cowboy Hat / Cap   Choices: Necklace / <u>Helmet</u> / Gloves / Ring   (Worn On Head)

- transportation (i.e., where things travel, land/water/air; do they have wheels?)

Cruise Ship / Yacht / Kayak   Choices: <u>Canoe</u> / Port / Dock / Jeep   (Travel On Water)

<u>3. SENTENCE COMPLETION</u> Directions: First, read the sentence. There is a missing word. Which answer choice goes best in the sentence? (Read the sentences and choices to your child. They may read along silently.)

If you aren't _____ with the vase, it will break.

A. careless   B. careful   C. clear   D. risky   E. sloppy

Explanation Here, your child must use the information in the sentence and make inferences (i.e., make a best guess based on the information) and select the best answer choice to fill in the blank. Be sure your child:
- pays attention to each word in the sentence and to each answer choice
- after making his/her choice, (s)he re-reads the complete sentence to ensure the choice makes the *most* sense compared to the other choices (the answer is B)

NON-VERBAL BATTERY

<u>4. FIGURE ANALOGIES</u> Directions: Look at the top set of pictures. They go together in some way. Look at the bottom set. The answer is missing. Figure out which answer choice would make the bottom set go together in the same way that the top set goes together.

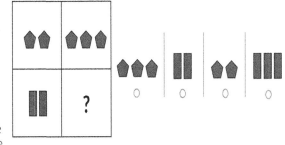

Explanation Come up with a "rule" describing how the top set is related. This "rule" shows how the figures in the left box "change" into the figures in the right box. On the left are 2 pentagons. On the right are 3 pentagons. The rule/change is that one more of the same kind of shape is added. On the bottom are 2 rectangles. The first choice is incorrect, it shows 3 pentagons (not the same shape). The second choice is incorrect (it only shows 2 rectangles). The third choice is incorrect - it has 2 pentagons. The last choice is correct. It has one more of the same shapes from the left box.

Here is a list of <u>basic</u> Figure Analogy "changes." (Test questions include this logic, but questions are more challenging.)

1. Color

2. Size

3. Amount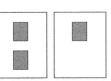

4. Color Reversal

5. Whole: Part

6. Number of Shape Sides

7. Rotation: 90° clockwise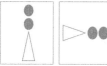

8. Rotation: 90° counter-clockwise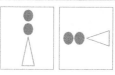

9. Line Direction

10. Flip / Mirror Image

11. Two Changes: Rotation & Quantity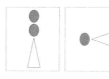

12. Two Changes: Rotation & Color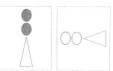

5. FIGURE CLASSIFICATION
Directions: The top row of pictures is alike in some way. Which picture on the bottom row goes best with the pictures on top?

Explanation Try to come up with a "rule" describing how the figures in the top row are alike. Then, see which choice follows the rule. If more than one choice would, then a more specific rule is needed. Here is 1 white triangle, 1 lightly shaded triangle, and 1 dark triangle. These are alike because they are all triangles. The first choice is correct because it's a triangle. None of the other are.

Below is a list of basic characteristics to analyze in Figure Classification questions.

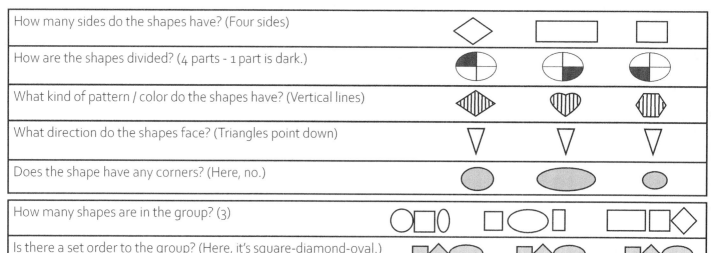

How many sides do the shapes have? (Four sides)	
How are the shapes divided? (4 parts - 1 part is dark.)	
What kind of pattern / color do the shapes have? (Vertical lines)	
What direction do the shapes face? (Triangles point down)	
Does the shape have any corners? (Here, no.)	
How many shapes are in the group? (3)	
Is there a set order to the group? (Here, it's square-diamond-oval.)	

6. PAPER FOLDING
Directions: The top row of pictures shows a sheet of paper. It was folded, then holes were made in it. Which bottom row picture shows how the unfolded paper would look?

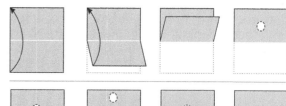

Explanation The first choice shows how it would look - 2 holes in the correct position. In the second choice, the holes are too close to the edge. In the third and fourth choices, there's only 1 hole.
• Make sure your child pays attention to: how many times the paper is folded, the number of shapes cut out, where these shapes are on the paper, and the direction they are facing.
• If possible, do a few examples with real paper and a hole puncher.
• Below are some basic examples to introduce Paper Folding logic.

Question (How Paper Is Folded)   Answer

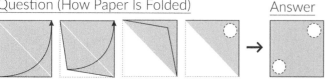

Note that 1 fold creates 2 holes.

Question (How Paper Is Folded)   Answer

Note the change in direction of the triangle once unfolded.

Question (How Paper Is Folded)   Answer   Question (How Paper Is Folded)   Answer

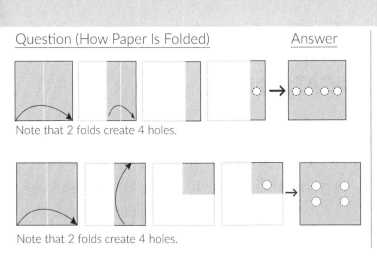

Note that 2 folds create 4 holes.

Note the change in direction of the triangles once unfolded.

Note that 2 folds create 4 holes.

Note the change in direction of the "points" once unfolded.

QUANTITATIVE BATTERY

7. NUMBER PUZZLES   Directions: What answer choice should you put in the place of the question mark so that both sides of the equal sign total the same amount?

Explanation   These questions have two formats. The first example is a fairly standard math problem and self-explanatory. In the second example, your child should first replace the black shape with its number value. If your child gets stumped on any Number Puzzles, (s)he can always test out each answer to find the one that works.

1. $10 = 25 - ?$ A. 25   B. 15   C. 20   D. 5   E. 0

2. $? = \blacklozenge + 2$ A. 1   B. 2   C. 3   D. 0   E. 4

     $\blacklozenge = 1$

8. NUMBER SERIES   Directions: Which answer choice would complete the pattern?

15   13   11   9   7   ?

A.1   B.3   C.5   D.6   E.4

Explanation   The numbers have made a pattern. To help your child figure out the pattern, have them write the difference between each number and the next. In this basic example, the pattern is: -2. In easier questions, the difference between all consecutive numbers is the same (i.e., the difference between 15 & 13 = 2 and between 13 & 11 = 2). However, sometimes the difference will not continuously repeat itself, as in these examples:

9   8   6   5   3   2   ?   The pattern is: -1, -2, -1, -2, etc. & the answer is 0.

1   2   4   7   11   16   ?   The pattern is: +1, +2, +3, +4, etc. & the answer is 22.

4   5   9   4   5   9   ?   The pattern is: 4-5-9 & the answer is 4.

9. NUMBER ANALOGIES   Directions: Look at the first two sets of numbers. Come up with a rule that both of these sets follow. Take this rule to figure out which answer choice goes in the place of the question mark.

[10 → 5]   [8 → 4]   [14 → ?]   A. 2   B. 7   C. 28   D. 16   E. 1

Explanation   Come up with a rule to explain how the first number "changes" into the second. It could use addition, subtraction, multiplication, or division. Have your child write the rule by *each* pair. Make sure it works with *both* pairs. The rule is "÷ by 2", so 7 is the answer.

- PRACTICE TEST 1 (WORKBOOK FORMAT) BEGINS ON THE NEXT PAGE -

VERBAL CLASSIFICATION

Directions: *(Read these out loud to your child. (S)he may read along silently.)* Look at the three words on the top row. Figure out how the words are alike. Next, look at the words in the row of answer choices. Which word goes best with the three words in the top row?

Parent note: Together, try to come up with a "rule" to describe how the top three words are alike and go together. Then, take this "rule," and figure out which of the answer choices would best follow that same rule. If your child finds that more than one choice follows the rule, then (s)he should try to come up with a rule that is more specific.

Example (#1): How do the words "South America," "Australia," and "Asia" go together? What is a rule that describes how they go together? These are all continents. Which of the answer choices would follow this rule? "Europe." Europe is the only choice that is a continent.

Make sure your child does not choose "continent." This is a frequent mistake that test-takers would make. It is not the actual answer choice that would follow the rule. "Continent" is the rule.

1   **South America**   **Australia**   **Asia**

    Ⓐ continent   Ⓑ atlas   Ⓒ Central America   Ⓓ India   Ⓔ Europe

2   **ladybug**   **wasp**   **mosquito**

    Ⓐ robin   Ⓑ butterfly   Ⓒ tick   Ⓓ spider   Ⓔ worm

3   **cone**   **pyramid**   **cylinder**

   Ⓐ sphere   Ⓑ pentagon   Ⓒ shape   Ⓓ diamond   Ⓔ geometric

4   **palm**   **wrist**   **thumb**

   Ⓐ elbow   Ⓑ neck   Ⓒ face   Ⓓ leg   Ⓔ finger

5   **oak**   **pine**   **palm**

   Ⓐ forest   Ⓑ log   Ⓒ tree   Ⓓ maple   Ⓔ lumber

6   **infant**   **chick**   **puppy**

   Ⓐ dog   Ⓑ rooster   Ⓒ fawn   Ⓓ pet   Ⓔ mammal

7   **comet**   **planet**   asteroid

   Ⓐ star   Ⓑ telescope   Ⓒ **astron**aut   Ⓓ laser   Ⓔ darkness

8   **cherry**   **apple**   **orange**

   Ⓐ yellow   Ⓑ color   Ⓒ fruit   Ⓓ lemon   Ⓔ strawberry

9   **chilly**   **hot**   **cold**

   Ⓐ wet   Ⓑ thermometer   Ⓒ freeze   Ⓓ cool   Ⓔ weather

10   **feathers**   **hair**   **scales**

   Ⓐ legs   Ⓑ skin   Ⓒ animal   Ⓓ claw   Ⓔ fur

11   **rhombus**   **trapezoid**   **rectangle**

   Ⓐ hexagon   Ⓑ parallelogram   Ⓒ prism   Ⓓ triangle   Ⓔ oval

12 evergreen   moss   fern

Ⓐ sunflower   Ⓑ leaf   Ⓒ stem   Ⓓ root   Ⓔ green

13 claw   talon   hoof

Ⓐ leg   Ⓑ feather   Ⓒ paw   Ⓓ trunk   Ⓔ footprint

14 baseball   volleyball   soccer

Ⓐ golf   Ⓑ tennis   Ⓒ gymnastics   Ⓓ diving   Ⓔ football

15 hood   tire   windshield wiper

Ⓐ headlight   Ⓑ seatbelt   Ⓒ steering wheel   Ⓓ radio   Ⓔ airbag

16 tornado   cyclone   blizzard

Ⓐ rain   Ⓑ hurricane   Ⓒ wind   Ⓓ weather   Ⓔ snow

17 basement   roots   mine

Ⓐ balcony   Ⓑ mountain   Ⓒ bridge   Ⓓ tunnel   Ⓔ runway

18 coach   teacher   instructor

Ⓐ assignment   Ⓑ school   Ⓒ driver   Ⓓ officer   Ⓔ tutor

19 dip   sink   dive

Ⓐ raise   Ⓑ jump   Ⓒ swell   Ⓓ drop   Ⓔ cut

20 truck   train   tricycle

Ⓐ road   Ⓑ wheel   Ⓒ car   Ⓓ track   Ⓔ trail

VERBAL ANALOGIES

Directions *(Read these out loud to your child. (S)he may read along silently.)* Look at the first set of words. Try to figure out how they belong together. Next, look at the second set of words. The answer is missing. Figure out which answer choice would make the second set go together in the same way that the first set goes together.

Parent note: Analogies compare sets of items, and the way they are related can easily be missed. Work through these together with your child so (s)he sees how the first set is related. Together, try to come up with a "rule" to describe how the first set is related. Then, in the second set, look at the first word. Take this "rule," use it together with the first word, and figure out which of the answer choices would follow that same rule. For answer choices that do not follow this rule, eliminate them. If your child finds that more than one choice follows this rule, then try to come up with a rule that is more specific.

Example (#1): How do the words "afternoon" and "night" go together? What is a rule that describes how they go together? The afternoon happens before the night. The first word happens before the second word. Look at the word "fall." Which of the choices follow this rule? "Fall" happens before what? Winter.

1   **afternoon → night : fall →**

    Ⓐ summer   Ⓑ autumn   Ⓒ winter   Ⓓ spring   Ⓔ season

2   **sweep → broom : weigh →**

    Ⓐ mop   Ⓑ scale   Ⓒ pounds   Ⓓ height   Ⓔ ruler

3   **Pacific → Atlantic : Asia →**

    Ⓐ Japan   Ⓑ India   Ⓒ Europe   Ⓓ Arctic   Ⓔ continent

4   **soap → hands : toothpaste →**

    Ⓐ lips   Ⓑ floss   Ⓒ toothbrush   Ⓓ teeth   Ⓔ water

5 cyclist → bicycle : surfer →

Ⓐ wave   Ⓑ board   Ⓒ beach   Ⓓ splash   Ⓔ athlete

6 cobra → crocodile : raccoon →

Ⓐ horse   Ⓑ chicken   Ⓒ lizard   Ⓓ turtle   Ⓔ grasshopper

7 diamond → gem : silver →

Ⓐ gold   Ⓑ necklace   Ⓒ shiny   Ⓓ metal   Ⓔ rock

8 duck → migrate : bear →

Ⓐ hibernate   Ⓑ grizzly   Ⓒ growl   Ⓓ mammal   Ⓔ walk

9 cello → instrument : cactus →

Ⓐ desert   Ⓑ tree   Ⓒ thorn   Ⓓ plant   Ⓔ bush

10 team → player : month →

Ⓐ calendar   Ⓑ week   Ⓒ year   Ⓓ April   Ⓔ twelve

11 helmet → head : seatbelt →

Ⓐ car   Ⓑ seat   Ⓒ waist   Ⓓ safety   Ⓔ click

12 horse → neigh : frog →

Ⓐ leap   Ⓑ jump   Ⓒ amphibian   Ⓓ tadpole   Ⓔ croak

13 restaurant → waiter : hospital →

Ⓐ nurse   Ⓑ clinic   Ⓒ waitress   Ⓓ dentist   Ⓔ architect

14   captain → boat : mayor →

     Ⓐ leader   Ⓑ country   Ⓒ city   Ⓓ election   Ⓔ president

15   straight → crooked : interior →

     Ⓐ exterior   Ⓑ inside   Ⓒ narrow   Ⓓ location   Ⓔ curvy

16   singer → concert : actress →

     Ⓐ actor   Ⓑ stage   Ⓒ director   Ⓓ movie   Ⓔ performer

17   savanna → zebra : rainforest →

     Ⓐ jungle   Ⓑ crocodile   Ⓒ parrot   Ⓓ snake   Ⓔ gorilla

18   child → children : this →

     Ⓐ these   Ⓑ that   Ⓒ those   Ⓓ think   Ⓔ where

19   poet → poem : chef →

     Ⓐ ingredient   Ⓑ journal   Ⓒ oven   Ⓓ measurement   Ⓔ meal

20   happy → elated : wet →

     Ⓐ moist   Ⓑ drenched   Ⓒ damp   Ⓓ rained   Ⓔ cleaned

21   bush → root : building →

     Ⓐ basement   Ⓑ level   Ⓒ room   Ⓓ house   Ⓔ construction

22   colossal → tiny : opaque →

     Ⓐ white   Ⓑ cloudy   Ⓒ light   Ⓓ vivid   Ⓔ transparent

SENTENCE COMPLETION

Directions
(Read these out loud to your child. (S)he may read along silently.)
First, read the sentence. There is a missing word. Next, look at the row of answer choices below the sentence. Which word would go best in the sentence?

Parent Note
At first glance, these questions may seem similar to fill-in-the-blank questions that test vocabulary acquisition. This section is not intended to be a vocabulary test.
You will notice that the language used in some questions is actually quite simple. While advanced vocabulary skills certainly will help with Sentence Completion questions, this section of the book tests your child's **reasoning skills** as well.

1   To make the cookie dough, we had to _____ sugar, flour, eggs, and other ingredients using the mixer.

   Ⓐ divide   Ⓑ measure   Ⓒ combine   Ⓓ heat   Ⓔ taste

2   The final competition between the _____ will decide the champion.

   Ⓐ rivals   Ⓑ allies   Ⓒ referees   Ⓓ judges   Ⓔ umpires

3 As we descended into the cave, the amount of natural light from the outside slowly _____.

Ⓐ increased   Ⓑ decreased   Ⓒ grew   Ⓓ expanded   Ⓔ developed

4 The veterinarian will_____ medicine for our dog.

Ⓐ prescribe   Ⓑ deliver   Ⓒ take   Ⓓ define   Ⓔ impose

5 Keeping strawberries in the refrigerator will _____ the growth of mold.

Ⓐ spread   Ⓑ expect   Ⓒ assist   Ⓓ release   Ⓔ prevent

6 The lack of rain will _____ a drought.

Ⓐ cause   Ⓑ limit   Ⓒ form   Ⓓ ruin   Ⓔ undo

7   **Prior to the party, we must _____ these balloons with helium.**

Ⓐ seal   Ⓑ tie   Ⓒ inflate   Ⓓ decorate   Ⓔ connect

8   **Her _____ to win the election included spending more on advertisements than the other candidates.**

Ⓐ promise   Ⓑ agreement   Ⓒ meeting   Ⓓ strategy   Ⓔ vote

9   **I must _____ that you not eat another donut because you will get a belly ache.**

Ⓐ allow   Ⓑ insist   Ⓒ refuse   Ⓓ permit   Ⓔ promise

10   **We need to _____ the instructions because they are too complicated.**

Ⓐ advance   Ⓑ multiply   Ⓒ simplify   Ⓓ direct   Ⓔ add to

11   The temperature change in the desert can be _____ - scorching days followed by frigid nights.

(A) drastic   (B) mild   (C) forecast   (D) calm   (E) hot

12   The body's _____ organs are those considered necessary for survival.

(A) scientific   (B) vital   (C) optional   (D) urgent   (E) additional

13   Before learning to surf, it is _____ to be a skilled swimmer.

(A) fun   (B) unique   (C) voluntary   (D) inessential   (E) essential

14   The scientist needs to _____ the information gathered from the tests in order to reach a conclusion.

(A) experiment   (B) teach   (C) guess   (D) evaluate   (E) disprove

15   Because the election results are so close, one of the candidates may request a _____.

(A) race   (B) recount   (C) campaign   (D) victory   (E) speech

16   The toys have been selling so quickly that our stock of inventory is quickly _____.

Ⓐ diminishing   Ⓑ increasing   Ⓒ assembling   Ⓓ delivering   Ⓔ recovering

17   We _____ a delay due to road construction, so we departed 30 minutes earlier than usual.

Ⓐ doubted   Ⓑ anticipated   Ⓒ missed   Ⓓ postponed   Ⓔ rushed

18   You'll be able to read the _____ summary in the amount time it takes to recite the alphabet.

Ⓐ lengthy   Ⓑ long   Ⓒ concise   Ⓓ rambling   Ⓔ extensive

19   If the eye drops irritate your eyes, you should _____ using them.

Ⓐ endure   Ⓑ continue   Ⓒ ignore   Ⓓ tolerate   Ⓔ discontinue

20   The weather here is quite _____, so I keep everything from an umbrella and a jacket to sunglasses and sunscreen in my bag.

Ⓐ variable   Ⓑ predictable   Ⓒ cloudy   Ⓓ humid   Ⓔ likely

FIGURE CLASSIFICATION

Directions: Look at the three pictures on the top row. Figure out how the pictures are alike. Next, look at the pictures in the row of answer choices. Which picture goes best with the three pictures in the top row?

Parent note: As you did with Verbal Classification questions, together, try to come up with a "rule" to describe how the top pictures are alike and go together. Then, take this "rule," and figure out which of the answer choices would best follow that same rule. If your child finds that more than one choice follows the rule, then (s)he should try to come up with a rule that is more specific.

Common "rules" for the designs in Figure Classification include, but are not limited to:
- number of sides
- color or design
- position
- rounded vs. angled corners
- rotation or direction
- quantity
- size of figure/figure's parts
- shape order

Have a look at the Figure Classification explanation in this book's Introduction if you have not already.

Note on multiple elements: Frequently, your "rule" will consist of more than one element, combining (but not limited to) the list above, i.e.,: **position and quantity**, **quantity and type**, **design and type**.

Make sure to read through the Answer Key explanations which include additional examples of "rules"/"changes."

Example (#1): How do these 3 shapes go together? What is a rule that describes how they go together? Each of the 3 designs on top is made up a large outer shape with an inner shape (that is the same shape), then they are repeated below. Which answer choice on the bottom row follows this rule? Choice A does.

1

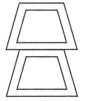      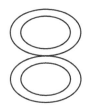

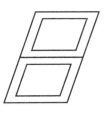   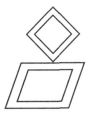   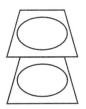      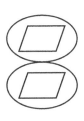

(A)   (B)   (C)   (D)   (E)

2

Ⓐ Ⓑ Ⓒ Ⓓ Ⓔ

3

 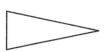

Ⓐ Ⓑ Ⓒ Ⓓ Ⓔ

4

Ⓐ Ⓑ Ⓒ Ⓓ Ⓔ

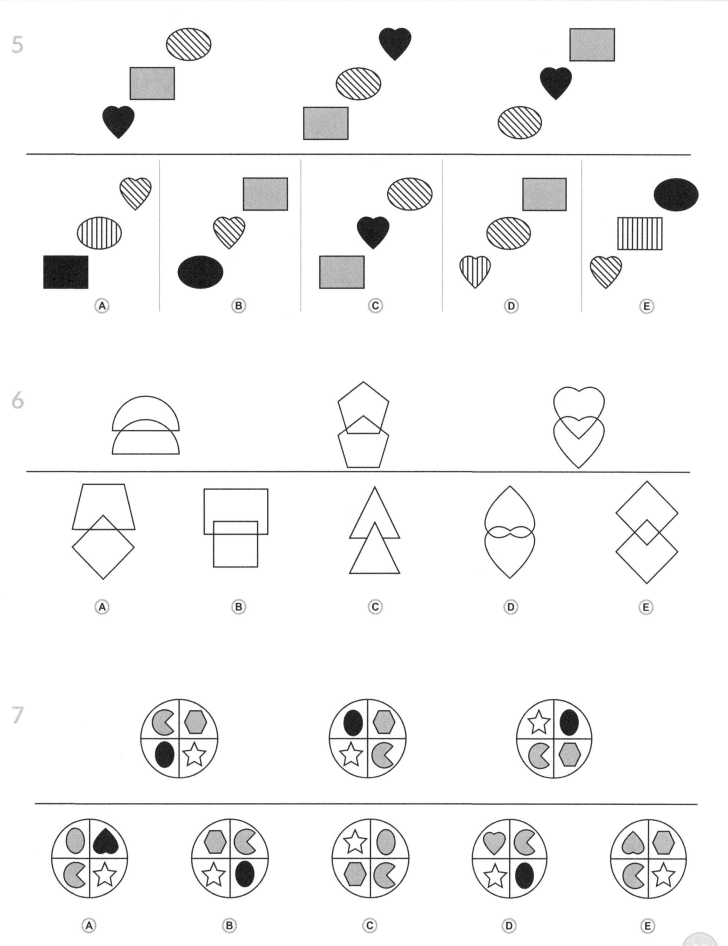

5

6

7

8

9

10

11

(A)   (B)   (C)   (D)   (E)

12

  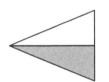

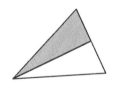 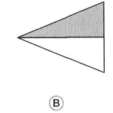 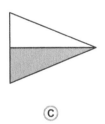 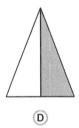 

(A)   (B)   (C)   (D)   (E)

13

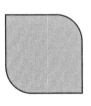  

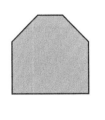    

(A)   (B)   (C)   (D)   (E)

14

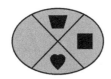  

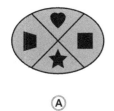 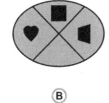 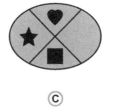 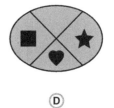 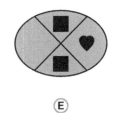

Ⓐ   Ⓑ   Ⓒ   Ⓓ   Ⓔ

15

   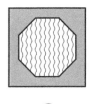

Ⓐ   Ⓑ   Ⓒ   Ⓓ   Ⓔ

16

Ⓐ   Ⓑ   Ⓒ   Ⓓ   Ⓔ

17

Ⓐ	Ⓑ	Ⓒ	Ⓓ	Ⓔ

18

Ⓐ	Ⓑ	Ⓒ	Ⓓ	Ⓔ

19

Ⓐ	Ⓑ	Ⓒ	Ⓓ	Ⓔ

20

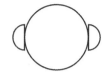 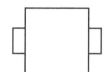

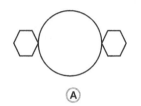 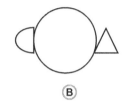 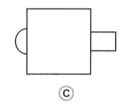 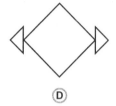 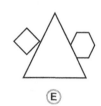

Ⓐ   Ⓑ   Ⓒ   Ⓓ   Ⓔ

21

 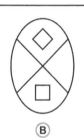   

Ⓐ   Ⓑ   Ⓒ   Ⓓ   Ⓔ

22

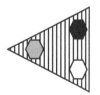 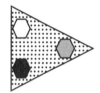 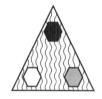

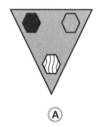 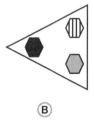 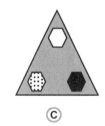 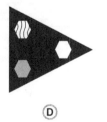 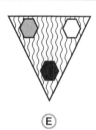

Ⓐ   Ⓑ   Ⓒ   Ⓓ   Ⓔ

FIGURE ANALOGIES

Directions: First, look at the top set of pictures. These belong together in some way. Next, look at the bottom picture. Then, decide which answer choice would make the bottom set of pictures go together in the same way as the top set. (The small arrow shows that the set goes together.)

Note: Use the same methodology here as Verbal Analogies. Together, come up with a "rule" to describe how the first set is related. (Tip: Try to see what "changes" from the first picture to the second picture.) Then, in the second set, look at the first picture. Take this "rule," use it together with the first picture in the second set, and figure out which of the answer choices follows it. If more than one choice follows this rule, then come up with a rule that is more specific.

You will see similar "rules" with Figure Analogies as with Figure Classification (see the previous section). As with Figure Classification, these rules will often involve more than one element (i.e., shape quantity, color(s) inside shape, shape position, number of shape sides, etc.).

Have a look at the Figure Analogies explanation in this book's Introduction if you have not already.

Make sure to read through the Answer Key explanations which include additional examples of "rules"/"changes".

Example (#1): In the top left box, the picture shows a black shape (a trapezoid) with a gray border around two of the sides. In the top right box, we see a similar shape, but what has changed? Here, the original shape has "flipped"/has become a mirror image. The rule is that the original figure "flips" to become a mirror image.

Look at the bottom left box. There is a shape group of 2 hearts, a large black heart and a small gray heart in the lower left side. How would this figure with the 2 hearts look if it "flipped"/became a mirror image? Which choice follows our rule? The answer where we see this rule is choice D. The shape group of 2 hearts has "flipped" to become a mirror image of the original shape group.

1

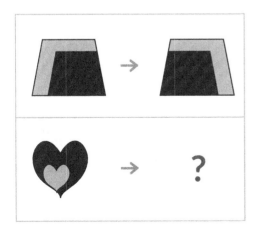

2

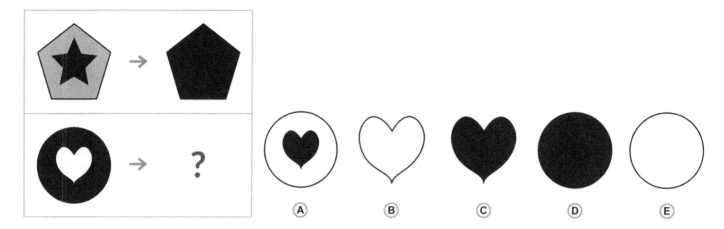

3

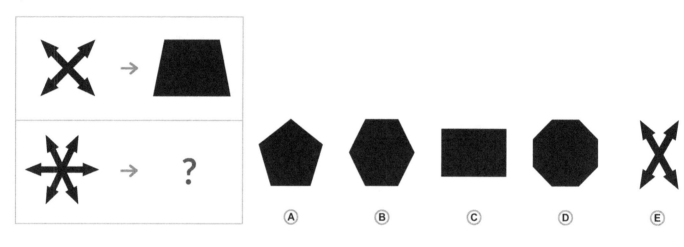

4

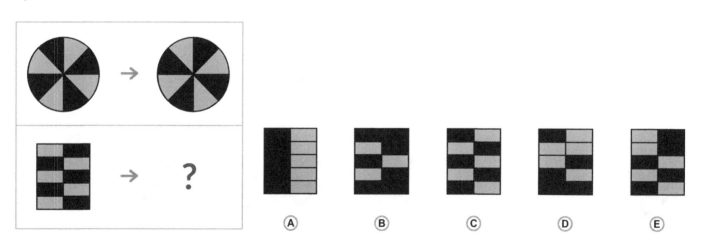

5

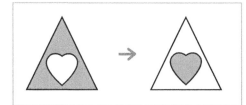

Ⓐ　　　Ⓑ　　　Ⓒ　　　Ⓓ　　　Ⓔ

6

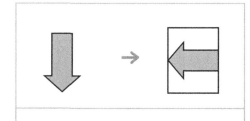

 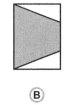 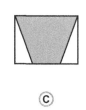 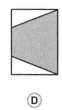 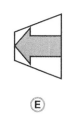

Ⓐ　　　Ⓑ　　　Ⓒ　　　Ⓓ　　　Ⓔ

7

Ⓐ　　　Ⓑ　　　Ⓒ　　　Ⓓ　　　Ⓔ

8

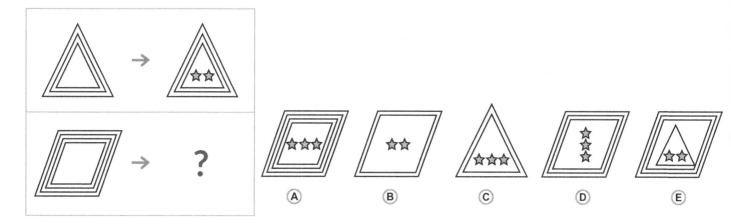

9

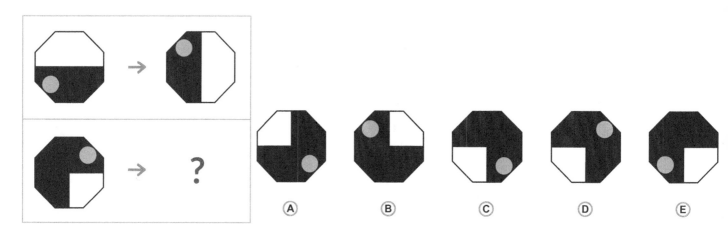

10

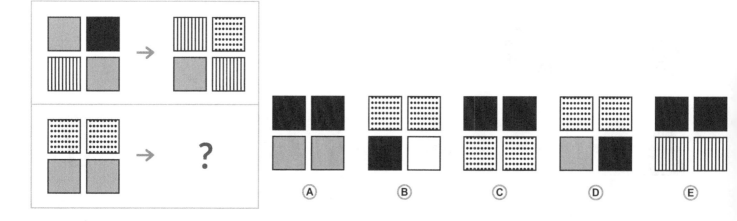

11

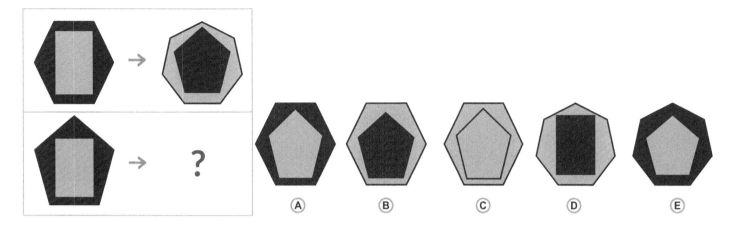

12

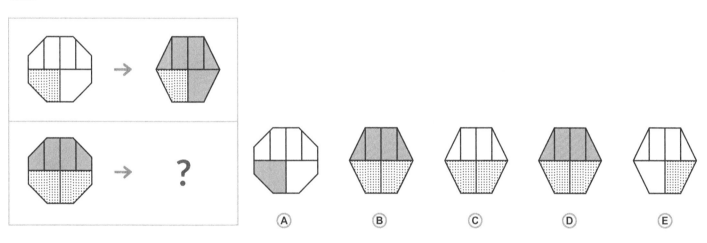

13

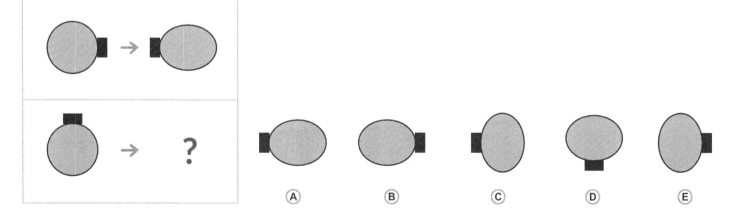

14

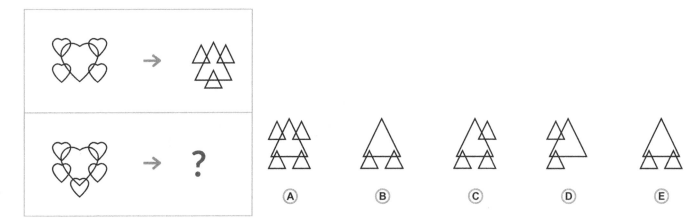

15

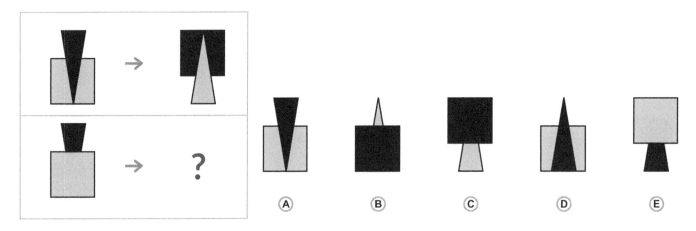

16

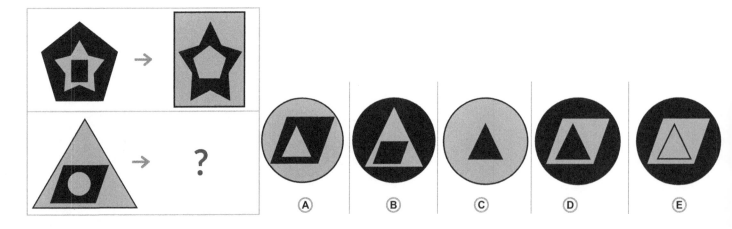

17

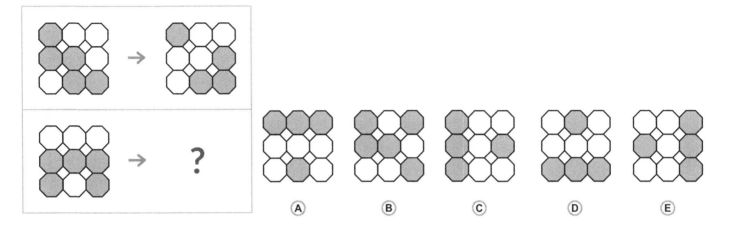

18

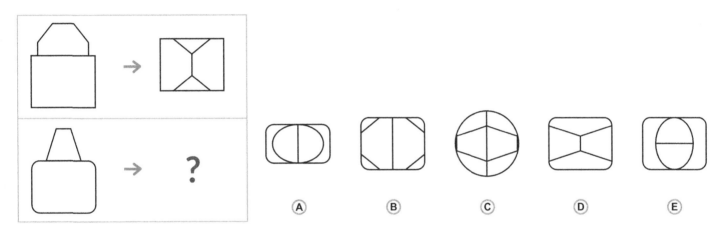

19

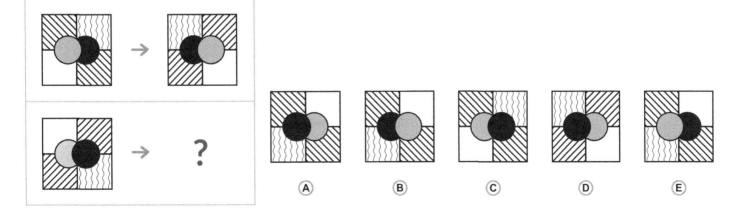

20

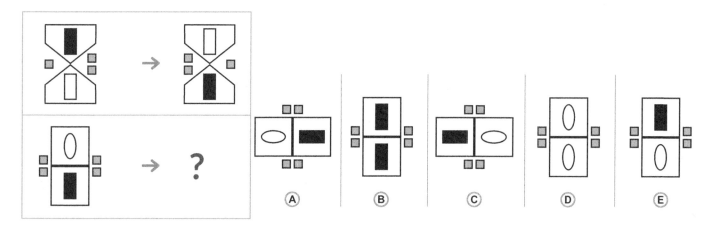

21

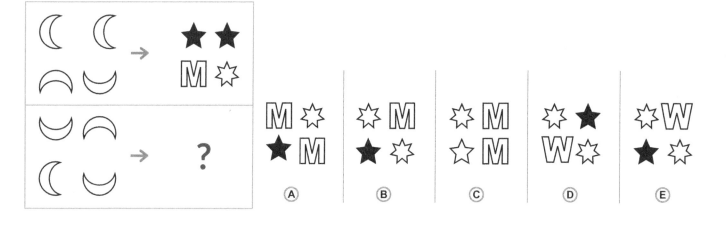

22

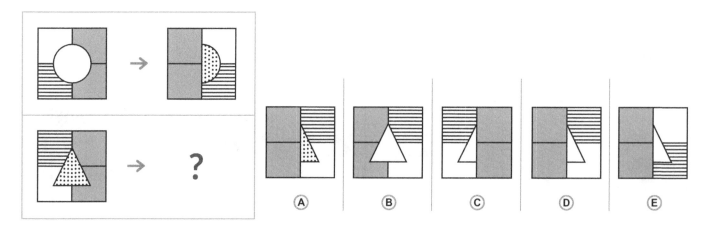

PAPER FOLDING

Directions: The top row of pictures shows a sheet of paper, how it was folded, and then how holes were made in it. Which picture on the bottom row shows how the paper would look after it is unfolded?

Note: To better understand the Paper Folding exercises, you may wish to use real paper and a hole puncher (or scissors). Be sure to notice:

- the number of times the paper is folded (for example, beginning with #6 some questions show the paper folded more than once)
- the hole placement
- the number of holes made in the paper

Have a look at the Paper Folding explanation in this book's Introduction if you have not already.

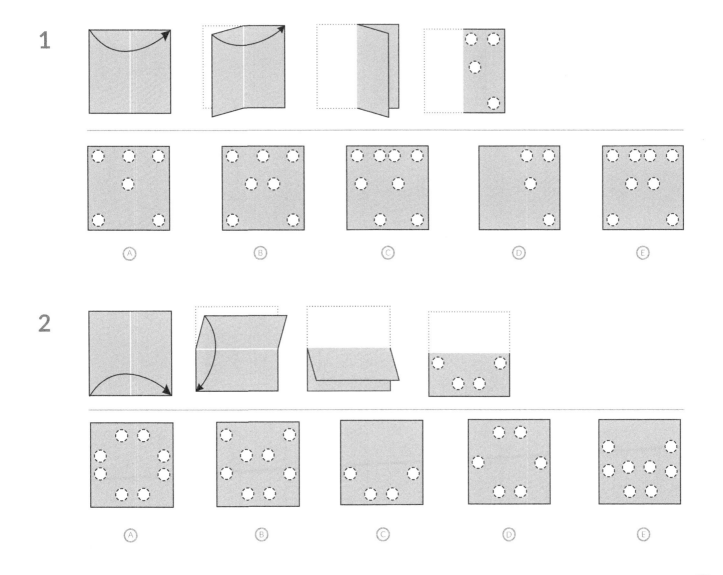

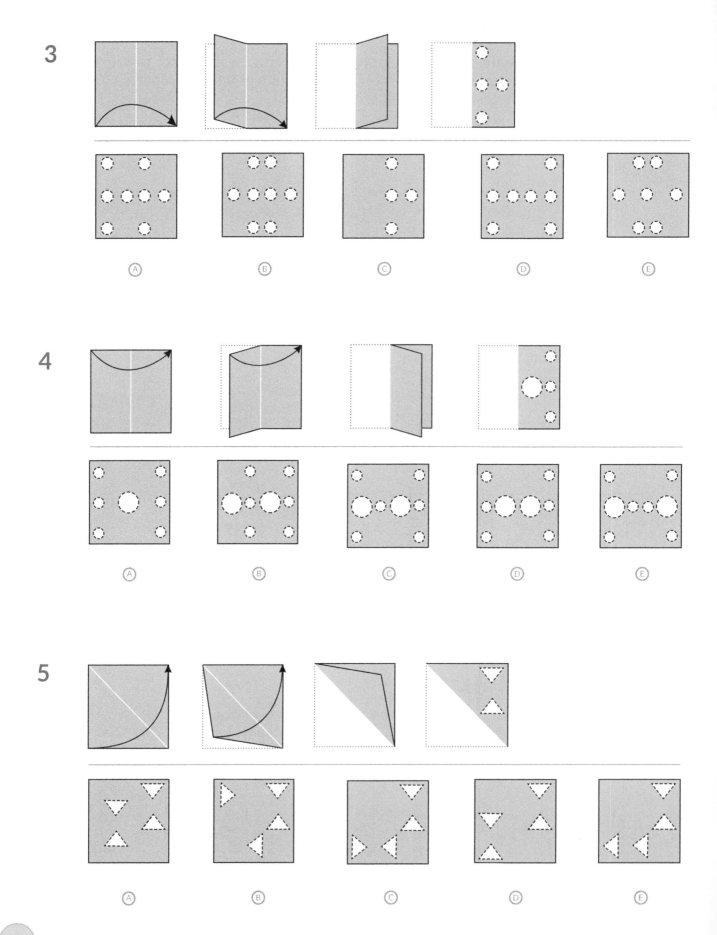

Parent note: Point out that in the questions below, the paper has been folded twice. (In the following pages, your child will need to pay close attention to whether the paper has been folded once or twice.)

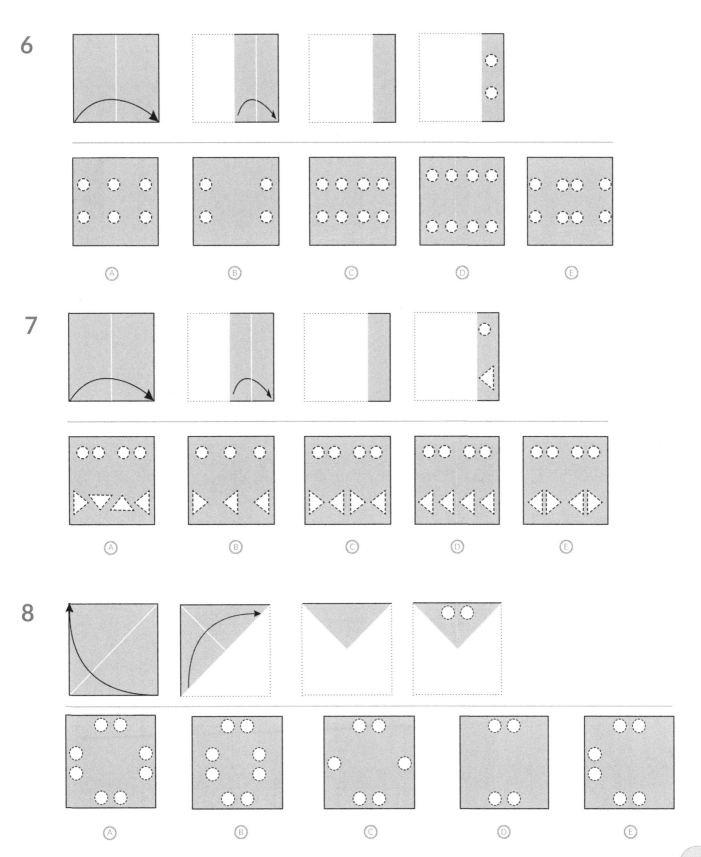

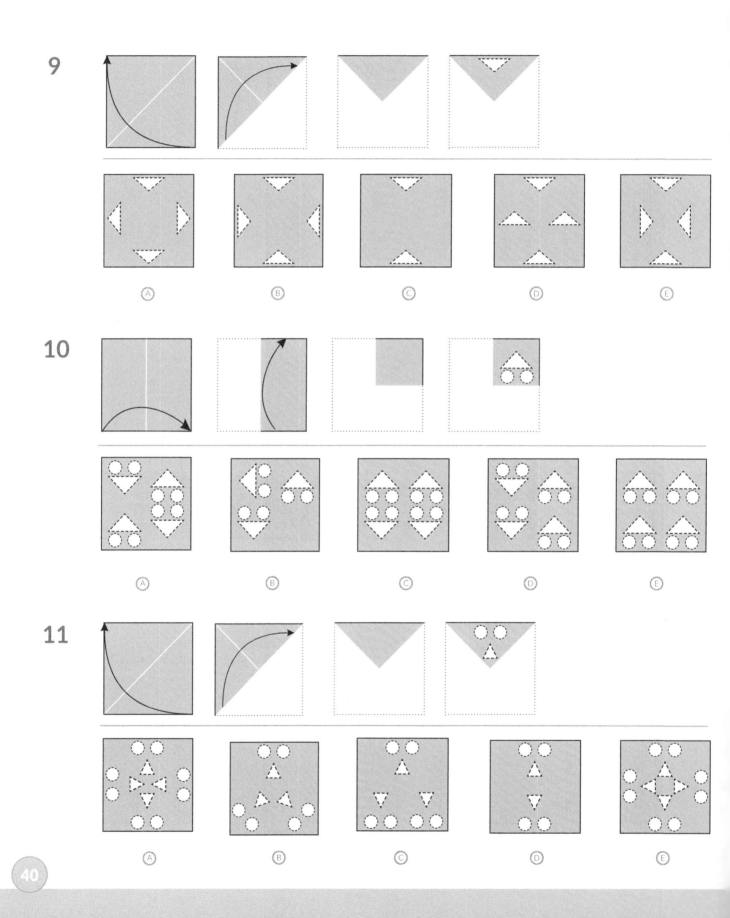

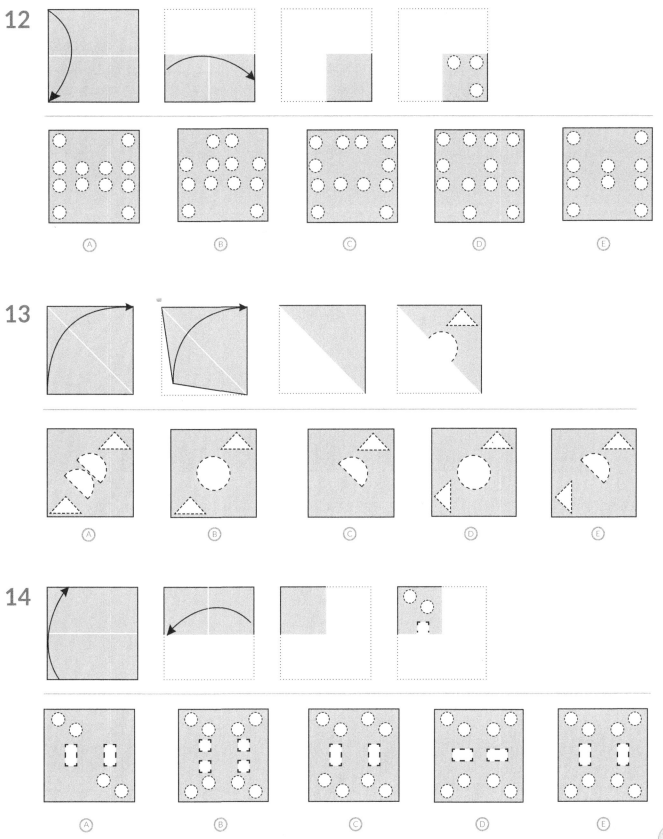

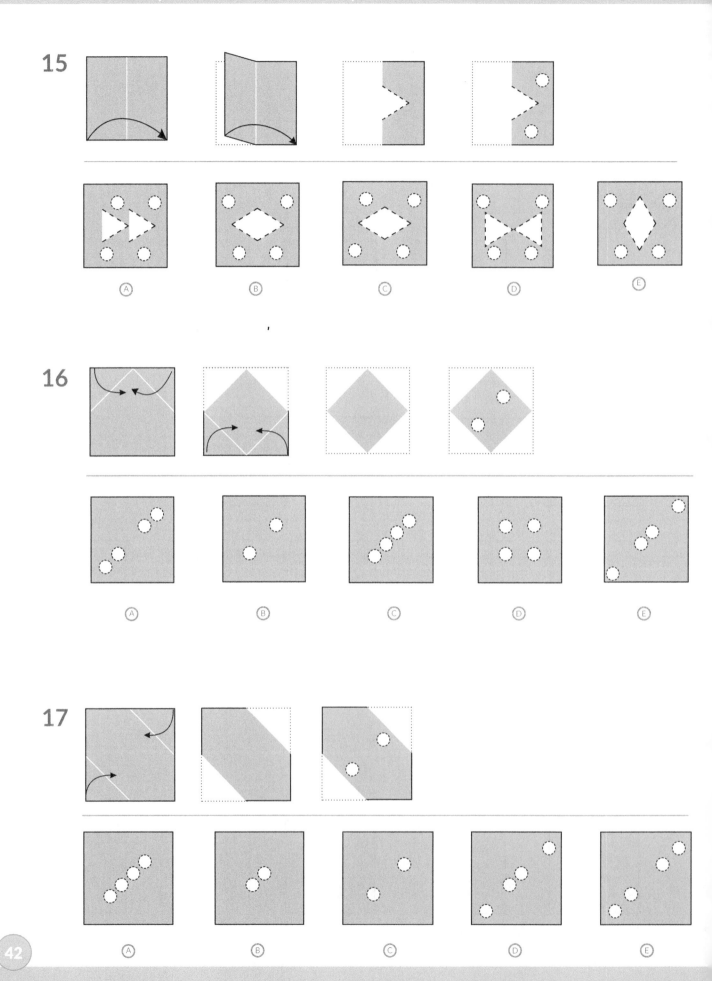

NUMBER PUZZLES

Directions: What answer choice should you put in the place of the question mark so that both sides of the equal sign total the same amount?

Note: As with math problems commonly seen in school, pay close attention to the signs. Do not make the simple mistake of performing the wrong operation (i.e., adding when you should actually be subtracting). Some questions have different operations (i.e., subtracting and division).

Double check your work by replacing the question mark with your answer.

With Number Puzzles questions, if your child gets "stumped", (s)he can always go through each answer choice, replacing the question mark with each choice, until (s)he finds the answer.

Example 1: The left side of the equal sign totals 42. Which answer choice do you need to put in the place of the question mark so that the right side of the equal sign totals 42? 6 times what number equals 42? 6 times 7 equals 42. So, the answer is 7.

Example 2: First, we need to replace the diamond with the correct number. We need to replace the diamond with 11. We see that the right side of the equation equals 33. What number do we need to put in place of the question mark so that the left side also equals 33? 22 plus 11 equals 33. So, the answer is 22.

1

$$42 \ = \ 6 \ \times \ \boxed{?}$$

○ 36   ○ 9   ○ 7   ○ 48   ○ 6

2

$$\boxed{?} \ + \ \blacklozenge \ = \ 33$$
$$\blacklozenge \ = \ 11$$

○ 22   ○ 3   ○ 44   ○ 10   ○ 32

3

$$7 \quad = \quad 63 \quad \div \quad \boxed{?}$$

○ 7   ○ 8   ○ 70   ○ 56   ○ 9

4

$$30 \quad - \quad 19 \quad = \quad 99 \quad \div \quad \boxed{?}$$

○ 49   ○ 50   ○ 9   ○ 12   ○ 11

5

$$\boxed{?} \quad + \quad 10 \quad = \quad 62 \quad - \quad 31$$

○ 83   ○ 29   ○ 21   ○ 39   ○ 49

6

$$32 \quad + \quad 8 \quad = \quad 25 \quad + \quad \boxed{?}$$

○ 5   ○ 15   ○ 65   ○ 17   ○ 40

7

$$3 \quad \times \quad 5 \quad = \quad 20 \quad - \quad \boxed{?}$$

○ 12   ○ 5   ○ 2   ○ 12   ○ 15

8

$$36 \div 9 = \boxed{?} \div 3$$

○ 27   ○ 45   ○ 9   ○ 12   ○ 4

9

$$8 \times 3 = \boxed{?} \times 4$$

○ 6   ○ 24   ○ 9   ○ 20   ○ 7

10

$$\blacklozenge - \boxed{?} = 9$$
$$\blacklozenge = 72$$

○ 81   ○ 53   ○ 63   ○ 8   ○ 72

11

$$\blacklozenge \times \boxed{?} = 56$$
$$\blacklozenge = 7$$

○ 9   ○ 63   ○ 49   ○ 64   ○ 8

12

$$1 + \boxed{?} = \blacklozenge$$
$$2 + \blacklozenge = 5$$

○ 5   ○ 3   ○ 2   ○ 1   ○ 0

13

$$? + 2 = 3 \times \blacklozenge$$

$$7 = \blacklozenge - 1$$

○ 19   ○ 22   ○ 7   ○ 16   ○ 24

14

$$4 + ? = 2 \times \blacklozenge$$

$$\blacklozenge - 1 = 6$$

○ 16   ○ 7   ○ 2   ○ 10   ○ 14

15

$$82 - ? = 5 \times \blacklozenge$$

$$18 - \blacklozenge = 6$$

○ 22   ○ 72   ○ 12   ○ 60   ○ 9

16

$$83 - ? = \blacklozenge$$

$$3 \times \blacklozenge = 45$$

○ 58   ○ 15   ○ 12   ○ 68   ○ 38

17

$$? = \blacklozenge + 4$$

$$5 = \blacklozenge - \bullet$$

$$\bullet = 1$$

○ 6   ○ 9   ○ 11   ○ 12   ○ 10

NUMBER ANALOGIES

Directions Look at the first two sets of numbers. Come up with a rule that both of these sets follow. Take this rule to figure out which answer choice goes in the place of the question mark.

Parent note: As with Verbal Analogies, your child must try to come up with a "rule" to answer the question. It must work with *all* the pairs. Be sure to test it on each one. The "rule" will involve standard math operations (subtraction, addition, division, or multiplication).

With all of the Number Analogies questions (as with all questions), it is very important to double check your work to ensure each number pair (and then the answer) follows the rule.

Example #1: In the first two sets you have 35 and 43, 49 and 57. How would you get from 35 to 43? How would you get from 49 to 57? In each, you add 8 to the first number. This is the "rule". Take this rule, look at the number at the beginning of the third set (21) and apply it to the bottom row of answer choices. What is the answer when you add 8 to 21? The answer is 29.

1   [35 → 43]   [49 → 57]   [21 → ?]

　　　○ 39　　　　○ 29　　　　○ 13　　　　○ 8　　　　○ 28

2   [95 → 90]   [49 → 44]   [30 → ?]

　　　○ 20　　　　○ 30　　　　○ 5　　　　○ 35　　　　○ 25

3   [22 → 11]   [6 → 3]   [18 → ?]

　　　○ 26　　　　○ 28　　　　○ 9　　　　○ 8　　　　○ 36

4 [6 → 30]   [8 → 40]   [5 → ?]

○ 0   ○ 10   ○ 1   ○ 5   ○ 25

5 [1 1/2 → 3]   [2 1/2 → 5]   [3 1/2 → ?]

○ 4 1/2   ○ 5   ○ 7   ○ 10   ○ 1/2

6 [15 → 5]   [21 → 7]   [6 → ?]

○ 18   ○ 2   ○ 3   ○ 10   ○ 13

7 [33 → 3]   [45 → 15]   [30 → ?]

○ 55   ○ 10   ○ 60   ○ 0   ○ 3

8 [1 → 0.5]   [4 → 2]   [6 → ?]

○ 3   ○ 2   ○ 1.5   ○ 12   ○ 16

9   [2/4 → 1/2]   [4/4 → 1]   [3/6 → ?]

○ 1   ○ 1/2   ○ 1/3   ○ 2   ○ 1/8

10   [6 → 60]   [3 → 30]   [1 → ?]

○ 110   ○ 15   ○ 11   ○ 100   ○ 10

11   [64 → 79]   [28 → 43]   [49 → ?]

○ 70   ○ 15   ○ 65   ○ 34   ○ 64

12   [11 → 22]   [50 → 100]   [14 → ?]

○ 7   ○ 2   ○ 28   ○ 50   ○ 6

13   [32 → 8]   [52 → 13]   [100 → ?]

○ 104   ○ 25   ○ 96   ○ 24   ○ 16

14   [3 → 36]   [1 → 12]   [5 → ?]

○ 52   ○ 50   ○ 12   ○ 60   ○ 17

15   [16 → 64]   [22 → 88]   [18 → ?]

○ 54   ○ 38   ○ 22   ○ 72   ○ 52

16   [88 → 79]   [65 → 56]   [81 → ?]

○ 9   ○ 90   ○ 72   ○ 77   ○ 104

17   [19 → 32]   [55 → 68]   [78 → ?]

○ 65   ○ 81   ○ 91   ○ 101   ○ 26

18   [2 → 40]   [4 → 80]   [6 → ?]

○ 12   ○ 120   ○ 40   ○ 180   ○ 20

19   [12 → 84]   [11 → 77]   [9 → ?]

○ 56   ○ 84   ○ 2   ○ 16   ○ 63

20   [96 → 12]   [64 → 8]   [40 → ?]

○ 6   ○ 48   ○ 32   ○ 5   ○ 8

21   [71 → 48]   [53 → 30]   [60 → ?]

○ 37   ○ 83   ○ 27   ○ 47   ○ 23

22   [72 → 12]   [90 → 15]   [42 → ?]

○ 26   ○ 36   ○ 7   ○ 48   ○ 6

23   [72 → 8]   [9 → 1]   [99 → ?]

○ 90   ○ 11   ○ 20   ○ 43   ○ 35

NUMBER SERIES

Directions: Here, you must try to figure out a pattern that the numbers have made. Which answer choice would complete the pattern?

Note: As with other questions types, it is helpful to figure out a "rule" that the numbers have made. In this section, it is a pattern. Use the "rule"/pattern to figure out the missing number. As with the Number Analogies, the rules will involve subtraction, addition, division, or multiplication.

Double check your work to ensure the series of numbers (and the answer) follows the rule/pattern.

Example #1: How do you get from 42 to 37, then from 37 to 32, then from 32 to 27, then from 27 to 22, and finally from 22 to 17? Each time, each number decreases by 5. If this is the pattern, then what would come after 17? It's Choice D, 12.

Note: Some of these are quite challenging and involve more than one "rule." They could even involve more than one kind of operation (addition/subtraction/multiplication/division). For example, the pattern in #4 involves two different numbers (+1, +2). The change between 3 and 4 is +1. The change between 4 and 6 is +2. This pattern is +1, +2, then it continues.

(Here, your child may also notice another pattern. The change between every other number is +3. The change between 3 and 6 is +3. The change between 6 and 9 is +3, etc. Then, the change between 4 and 7 is +3. The change bewteen 7 and 10 is +3.)

1　42　　37　　32　　27　　22　　17　　?

○ 4　　　○ 5　　　○ 20　　　○ 12　　　○ 13

2　3　　21　　39　　57　　75　　?

○ 95　　　○ 85　　　○ 103　　　○ 83　　　○ 93

3   **4**   **8**   **16**   **32**   **64**   **?**

○ 96   ○ 110   ○ 46   ○ 128   ○ 84

4   **3**   **4**   **6**   **7**   **9**   **10**   **12**   **?**

○ 12   ○ 13   ○ 10   ○ 14   ○ 11

5   **20**   **19**   **17**   **16**   **14**   **13**   **11**   **?**

○ 9   ○ 8   ○ 10   ○ 11   ○ 7

6   **-5**   **-4**   **-3**   **-2**   **-1**   **0**   **1**   **?**

○ -2   ○ -1   ○ 2   ○ 1   ○ 3

7   **1**   **20**   **1**   **21**   **1**   **22**   **?**

○ 1   ○ 23   ○ 0   ○ 24   ○ 2

8   **10**   **10**   **8**   **8**   **6**   **6**   **?**

○ 6   ○ 4   ○ 5   ○ 0   ○ 3

9   **10**   **11**   **16**   **17**   **22**   **23**   **28**   **?**

○ 30   ○ 24   ○ 39   ○ 33   ○ 29

10   **42**   **40**   **36**   **34**   **30**   **28**   **24**   **?**

○ 18   ○ 14   ○ 22   ○ 26   ○ 20

11   **30**   **31**   **32**   **34**   **35**   **36**   **38**   **?**

○ 41   ○ 42   ○ 38   ○ 39   ○ 40

12   **28**   **27**   **26**   **24**   **23**   **22**   **20**   **?**

○ 19   ○ 18   ○ 20   ○ 16   ○ 17

13   **3**   **10**   **3**   **15**   **3**   **20**   **3**   **?**

○ 30   ○ 3   ○ 25   ○ 5   ○ 4

14   **10.5**   **11.5**   **12.5**   **13.5**   **14.5**   **15.5**   **?**

○ 16.5   ○ 16.0   ○ 15.6   ○ 17.5   ○ 17.0

15   **25**   **24**   **22**   **19**   **15**   **10**   **?**

○ 9   ○ 1   ○ 2   ○ 4   ○ 3

16   **7**   **9**   **12**   **16**   **21**   **27**   **34**   **?**

○ 39   ○ 42   ○ 40   ○ 32   ○ 45

17   **1**   **10**   **2**   **11**   **3**   **12**   **4**   **13**   **5**   **?**

○ 17   ○ 15   ○ 6   ○ 12   ○ 14

18   **20**   **3**   **19**   **4**   **18**   **5**   **17**   **6**   **16**   **?**

○ 6   ○ 7   ○ 15   ○ 13   ○ 8

19   **10**   **-9**   **8**   **-7**   **6**   **-5**   **4**   **?**

○ 2   ○ 1   ○ 0   ○ -3   ○ 3

20   **91**   **81**   **85**   **75**   **79**   **69**   **73**   **63**   **67**   **?**

○ 61   ○ 47   ○ 71   ○ 77   ○ 57

21   **5**   **11**   **6**   **12**   **7**   **13**   **8**   **14**   **9**   **?**

○ 15   ○ 10   ○ 12   ○ 16   ○ 11

22   **7**   **20**   **8**   **19**   **9**   **18**   **10**   **17**   **11**   **?**

○ 12   ○ 16   ○ 15   ○ 11   ○ 19

23   **13**   **14**   **15**   **17**   **18**   **19**   **21**   **22**   **23**   **?**

○ 21   ○ 24   ○ 25   ○ 25   ○ 26

End of Practice Test 1 (Workbook Format). • Practice Test 2 begins on the next page.

Directions: The top 3 words go together in some way. Which answer choice goes best with the top words?

1   **chicken**   **ostrich**   **penguin**

(A) polar bear   (B) flamingo   (C) panda   (D) eggs   (E) fish

2   **socks**   **gloves**   **earrings**

(A) shirt   (B) scarf   (C) ring   (D) necklace   (E) skis

3   **bottle**   **mug**   **bowl**

(A) glass   (B) tea   (C) liquid   (D) plate   (E) strainer

4   **cactus**   **clover**   **emerald**

(A) soil   (B) mushroom   (C) grass   (D) rainbow   (E) sand

5   **deer**   **giraffe**   **squirrel**

(A) spider   (B) rhino   (C) ostrich   (D) beetle   (E) squid

6   **meter**   **second**   **pound**

(A) ruler   (B) road   (C) mile   (D) stopwatch   (E) measurement

7   **rope**   **mountain**   **stairs**

(A) rail   (B) elevator   (C) balcony   (D) hill   (E) up

8   **stool**   **rocking chair**   **throne**

(A) couch   (B) crown   (C) trunk   (D) shelf   (E) counter

9   **avenue**   **highway**   **interstate**

(A) travel   (B) street   (C) map   (D) garage   (E) subway

10   **architect**   **builder**   **electrician**

(A) chauffeur   (B) server   (C) carpenter   (D) cook   (E) customer

11   **carrot**   **turnip**   **potato**

ⓐ lettuce   ⓑ cabbage   ⓒ cucumber   ⓓ onion   ⓔ pumpkin

12   **jolly**   **joyful**   **merry**

ⓐ cheerful   ⓑ caring   ⓒ smile   ⓓ gift   ⓔ holiday

13   **harp**   **fiddle**   **cello**

ⓐ instrument   ⓑ guitar   ⓒ drums   ⓓ clarinet   ⓔ conductor

14   **usually**   **seldom**   **frequently**

ⓐ time   ⓑ schedule   ⓒ please   ⓓ probably   ⓔ often

15   **giant**   **short**   **towering**

ⓐ confident   ⓑ height   ⓒ weight   ⓓ small   ⓔ length

16   **emperor**   **king**   **chief**

ⓐ council   ⓑ tribe   ⓒ assistant   ⓓ reporter   ⓔ governor

17   **transport**   **move**   **transfer**

ⓐ package   ⓑ send   ⓒ truck   ⓓ port   ⓔ order

18   **peak**   **dome**   **roof**
ⓐ wall   ⓑ building   ⓒ crest   ⓓ base   ⓔ cellar

19   **bay**   **pond**   **swamp**

ⓐ stream   ⓑ canal   ⓒ dam   ⓓ bridge   ⓔ swimming pool

20   **tale**   **fable**   **myth**

ⓐ report   ⓑ article   ⓒ summary   ⓓ biography   ⓔ legend

Directions: Which choice makes the second set of words go together in the same way the first set does?

1   add → subtract : multiply →

Ⓐ array   Ⓑ number   Ⓒ times   Ⓓ addition   Ⓔ divide

2   hour → day : day →

Ⓐ Monday   Ⓑ month   Ⓒ minute   Ⓓ time   Ⓔ birthday

3   tuna → fish : pine →

Ⓐ tree   Ⓑ oak   Ⓒ forest   Ⓓ maple   Ⓔ grove

4   ship → cargo : subway →

Ⓐ train   Ⓑ station   Ⓒ conductor   Ⓓ passengers   Ⓔ tunnel

5   novel → chapter : play →

Ⓐ comedy   Ⓑ author   Ⓒ scene   Ⓓ director   Ⓔ theater

6   tricycle → wheel : triangle →

Ⓐ shape   Ⓑ side   Ⓒ pyramid   Ⓓ square   Ⓔ triple

7   positive → negative : ancient →

Ⓐ old   Ⓑ historic   Ⓒ fresh   Ⓓ early   Ⓔ modern

8   cover → book : envelope →

Ⓐ alphabet   Ⓑ letter   Ⓒ magazine   Ⓓ paragraph   Ⓔ table of contents

9   bird → feather : fish →

Ⓐ scale   Ⓑ fin   Ⓒ gill   Ⓓ bone   Ⓔ shell

10   field → corn : orchard →

Ⓐ carrot   Ⓑ apple   Ⓒ pumpkin   Ⓓ harvest   Ⓔ farm

11   clay → pottery : sand →

Ⓐ glass   Ⓑ water   Ⓒ beach   Ⓓ coral   Ⓔ shell

12   herd → buffalo : pack →

    Ⓐ cat   Ⓑ owl   Ⓒ frog   Ⓓ wolf   Ⓔ cow

13   thing → dozen : inch →

    Ⓐ centimeter   Ⓑ foot   Ⓒ eggs   Ⓓ yard   Ⓔ half

14   refrigerator → electricity : watch →

    Ⓐ wrist   Ⓑ time   Ⓒ clock   Ⓓ number   Ⓔ battery

15   duck → waddle : snake →

    Ⓐ slither   Ⓑ walk   Ⓒ hop   Ⓓ hiss   Ⓔ squeak

16   musicians → band : sailors →

    Ⓐ crew   Ⓑ vessel   Ⓒ ship   Ⓓ captain   Ⓔ army

17   cent → dollar : year →

    Ⓐ anniversary   Ⓑ century   Ⓒ walk   Ⓓ quarter   Ⓔ decade

18   court case → judge : basketball game →

    Ⓐ team   Ⓑ player   Ⓒ referee   Ⓓ coach   Ⓔ fan

19   truthful → honest : neutral →

    Ⓐ trustworthy   Ⓑ unbiased   Ⓒ clear   Ⓓ relaxed   Ⓔ strong

20   paddle → kayak : sail →

    Ⓐ yacht   Ⓑ canoe   Ⓒ propeller   Ⓓ oar   Ⓔ passenger

21   water → dry : light →

    Ⓐ lamp   Ⓑ wet   Ⓒ bright   Ⓓ dim   Ⓔ clear

22   compact → loose : opponent →

    Ⓐ friend   Ⓑ contestant   Ⓒ competition Ⓓ coach   Ⓔ ally

Directions: There is a missing word in the sentence. Which answer choice would go best in the sentence?

1   When preparing medicine, pharmacists must be _____ with their
    measurements.

    Ⓐ general   Ⓑ approximate   Ⓒ precise   Ⓓ generous   Ⓔ experimental

2   My parrot can _____ my voice so well that if you close your eyes, you
    cannot tell our voices apart.

    Ⓐ hear   Ⓑ replay   Ⓒ announce   Ⓓ direct   Ⓔ mimic

3   Compared to shorter buildings, tall buildings, due to their additional
    weight, require more _____ near the base.

    Ⓐ support   Ⓑ levels   Ⓒ height   Ⓓ ceilings   Ⓔ air

4   The apple harvest was abundant this year, so the farmer's market is _____ of
    apples.

    Ⓐ empty   Ⓑ full   Ⓒ lacking   Ⓓ banned   Ⓔ owed

5   Because the students _____ disobey instructions, the class will receive an
    award from the principal.

    Ⓐ frequently   Ⓑ generally   Ⓒ regularly   Ⓓ rarely   Ⓔ occasionally

6   Growing trees in _____locations is quite challenging.

    Ⓐ tropical   Ⓑ humid   Ⓒ sunny   Ⓓ arid   Ⓔ rural

7   Wearing a jacket will help you stay warm by _____ body heat.

    Ⓐ measuring   Ⓑ releasing   Ⓒ conserving   Ⓓ avoiding   Ⓔ noticing

8   The U.S. _____ the most land in 1803 when the country nearly doubled the amount of territory it controlled.

    Ⓐ gained   Ⓑ lost   Ⓒ donated   Ⓓ declined   Ⓔ created

9   Let's find a radio station that plays mostly music, instead of one that plays _____ ads.

    Ⓐ interesting   Ⓑ continuous   Ⓒ helpful   Ⓓ amusing   Ⓔ delightful

10   There are no permanent residents of Antarctica due to its ____ temperatures.

    Ⓐ moderate   Ⓑ cool   Ⓒ mild   Ⓓ mighty   Ⓔ extreme

11   Without a _____ description, the artist cannot create an accurate sketch of the suspect.

      Ⓐ vague   Ⓑ curious   Ⓒ dangerous   Ⓓ specific   Ⓔ loud

12   The _____ model of our town closely resembles the town's actual appearance.

      Ⓐ fictional   Ⓑ realistic   Ⓒ bizarre   Ⓓ strange   Ⓔ mystical

13   The _____ to Mount Everest, the world's tallest mountain, will last around two months.

      Ⓐ trail   Ⓑ path   Ⓒ safari   Ⓓ expedition   Ⓔ vacation

14   Because of the train's _____ schedule, do not depend on the train if you are going to the airport to catch a flight.

      Ⓐ irregular   Ⓑ dependable   Ⓒ set   Ⓓ rapid   Ⓔ steady

15   They chose to have the concert at a stadium due to the location's _____ amount of space.

      Ⓐ small   Ⓑ ample   Ⓒ scarce   Ⓓ restricted   Ⓔ musical

16   Eating broccoli, while not completely necessary for good health, is certainly
_____.

  Ⓐ beneficial   Ⓑ required   Ⓒ crucial   Ⓓ fresh   Ⓔ disagreeable

17   My parents bought a lottery ticket, even though it is highly _____ that they
will win the $100 million jackpot.

  Ⓐ apparent   Ⓑ likely   Ⓒ improbable   Ⓓ lucky   Ⓔ fortunate

18   The immense size of the _____ columns of the Roman temple is one of the
reasons the temple still stands today.

  Ⓐ frail   Ⓑ fragile   Ⓒ worthless   Ⓓ obsolete   Ⓔ massive

19   This restaurant offers _____ refills on lemonade, so drink as much of it as
you would like.

  Ⓐ unlimited   Ⓑ restricted   Ⓒ limited   Ⓓ ending   Ⓔ costly

20   The windy conditions resulted in the wildfire becoming even more _____.

  Ⓐ airy   Ⓑ stormy   Ⓒ rare   Ⓓ daring   Ⓔ destructive

Directions: Which picture in the bottom row goes best with the 3 pictures in the top row?

1

A   B   C   D   E

2

A   B   C   D   E

3

A   B   C   D   E

4

A   B   C   D   E

5

A   B   C   D   E

6

A   B   C   D   E

7

A B C D E

8

A B C D E

9

A B C D E

10

11

12

13

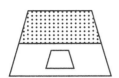 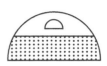

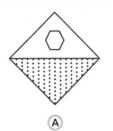 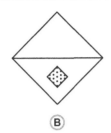 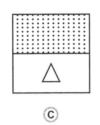 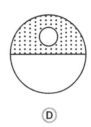 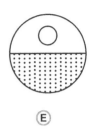

Ⓐ Ⓑ Ⓒ Ⓓ Ⓔ

14

Ⓐ Ⓑ Ⓒ Ⓓ Ⓔ

15

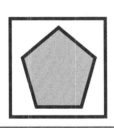  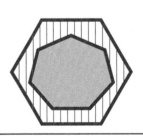

 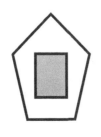   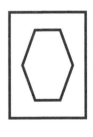

Ⓐ Ⓑ Ⓒ Ⓓ Ⓔ

16

17

18

19

20

    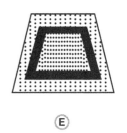

Ⓐ Ⓑ Ⓒ Ⓓ Ⓔ

21

 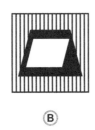   

Ⓐ Ⓑ Ⓒ Ⓓ Ⓔ

22

 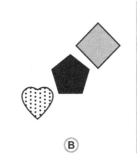  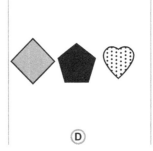 

Ⓐ Ⓑ Ⓒ Ⓓ Ⓔ

Directions: Which choice makes the second set of pictures go together in the same way as the first set?

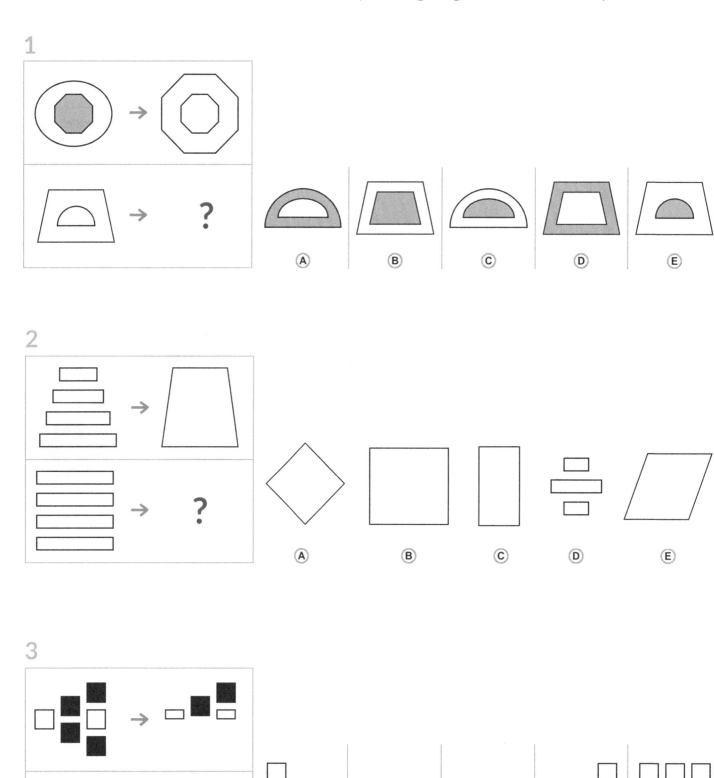

4

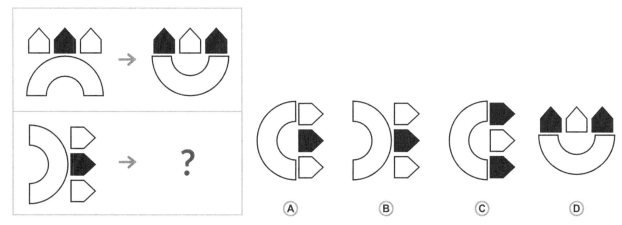

5

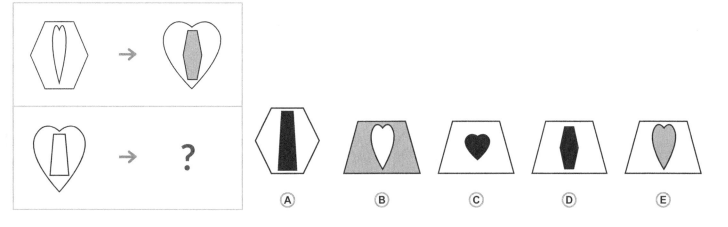

6

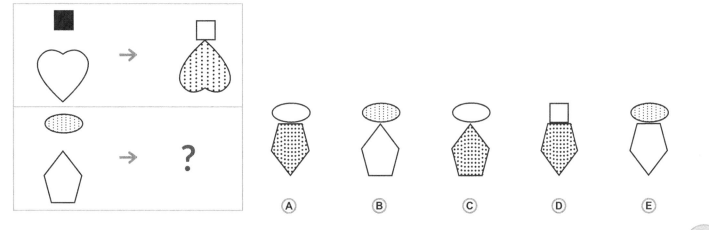

7

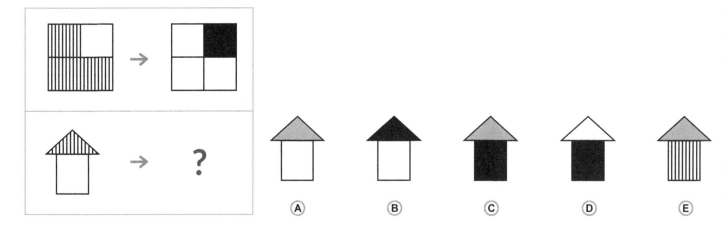

8

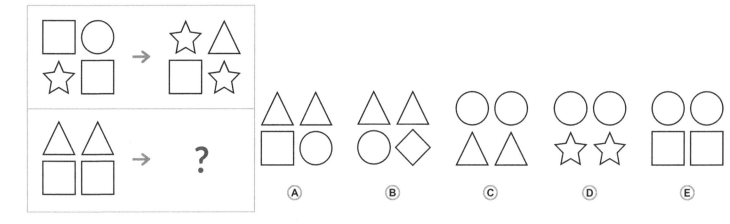

9

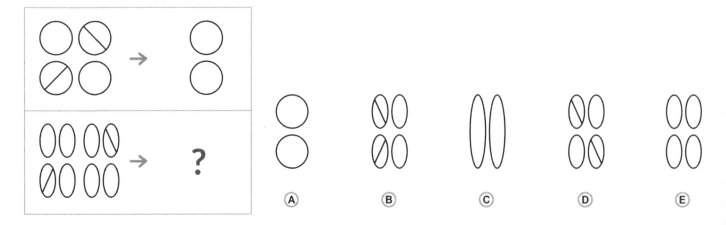

10

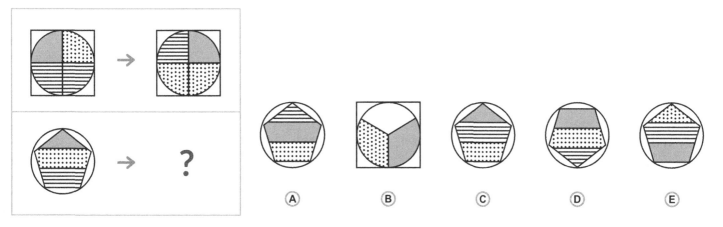

11

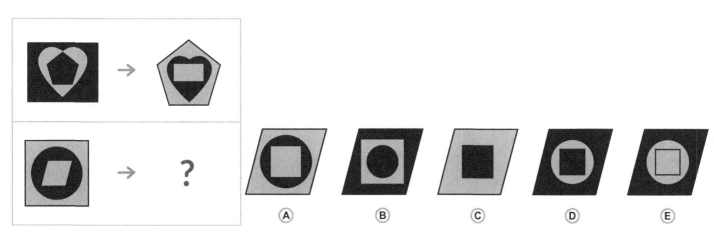

12

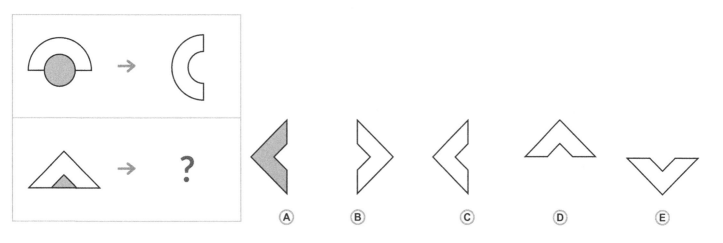

13

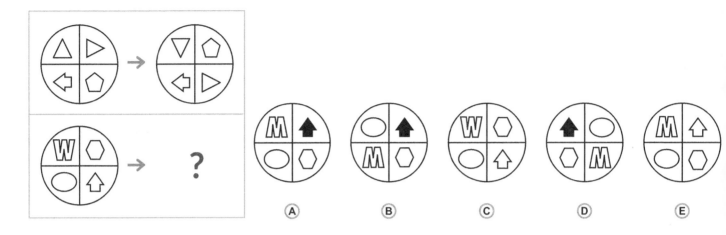

14

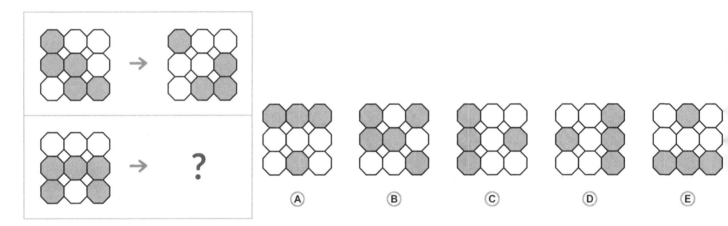

15

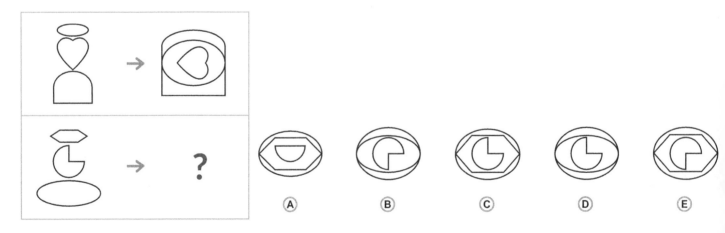

16

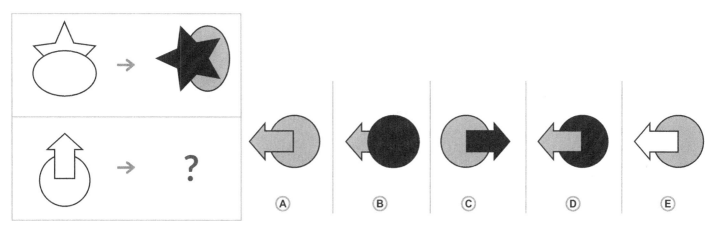

17

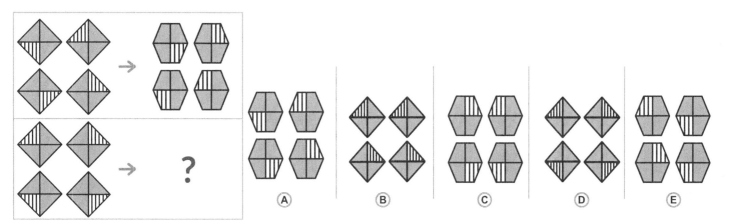

18

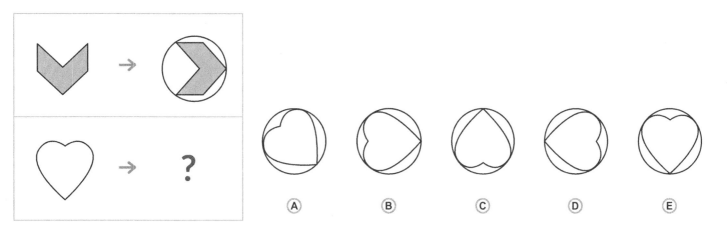

19

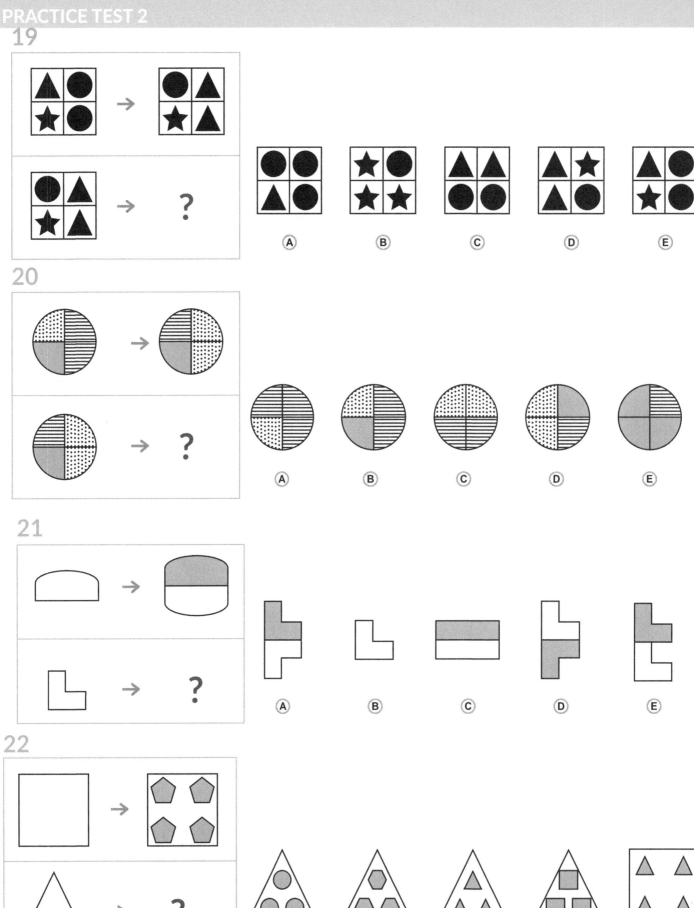

20

21

22

Directions: The top row shows a sheet of paper, how it was folded, and how holes were made in it. Which picture on the bottom row shows how the paper would look unfolded?

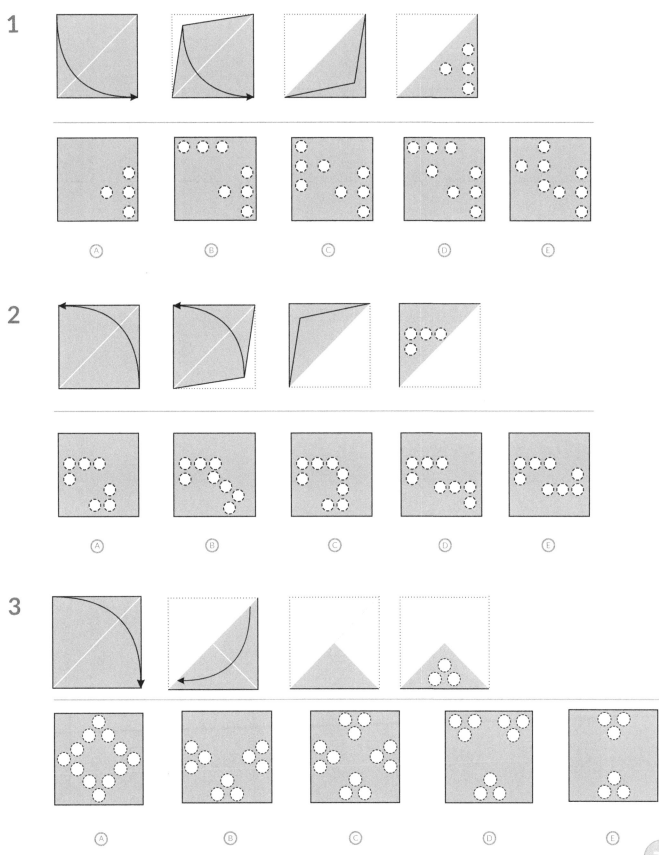

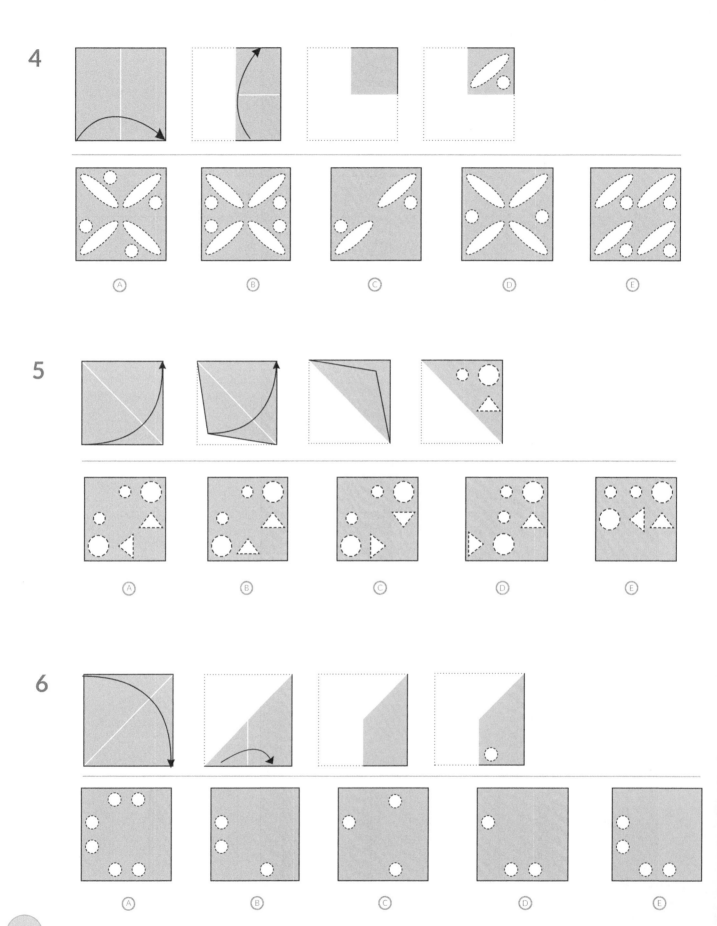

7

A   B   C   D   E

8

A   B   C   D   E

9

A   B   C   D   E

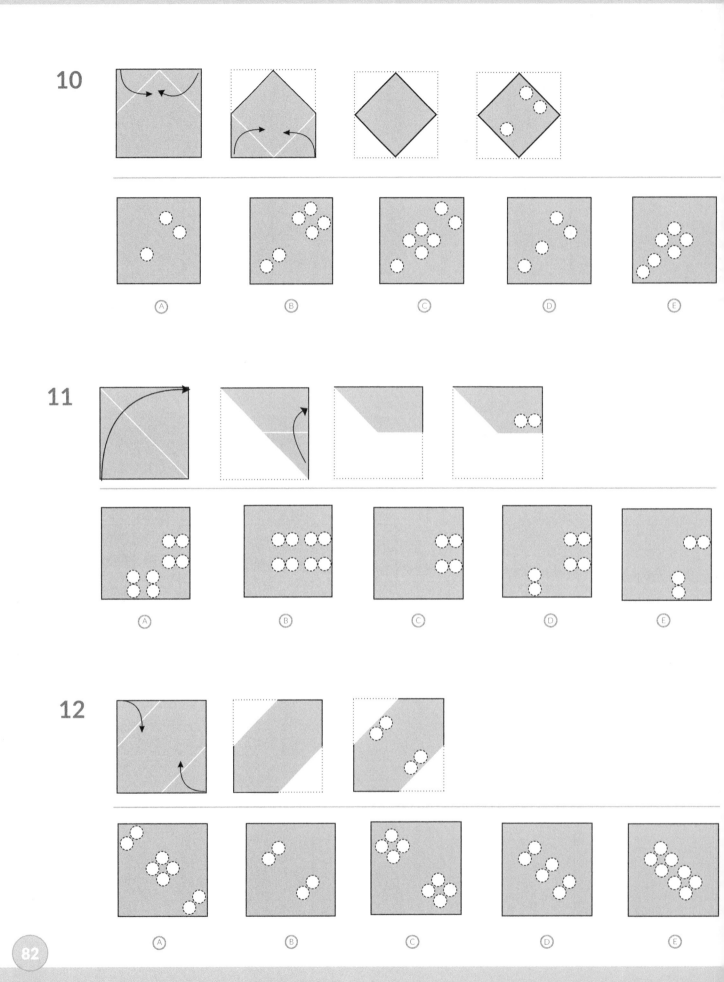

13

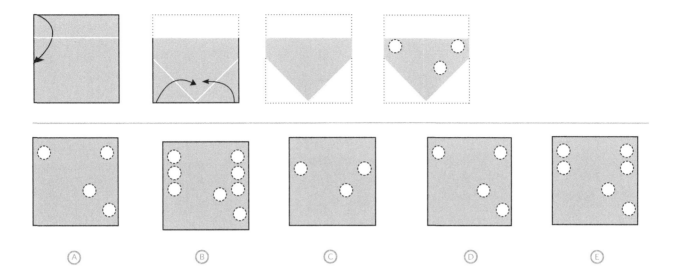

14

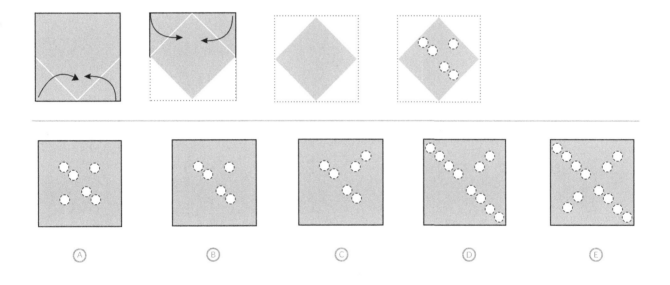

15

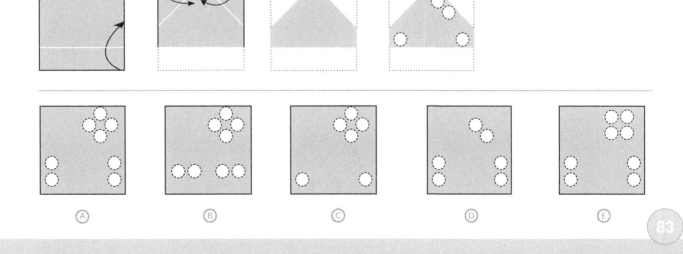

Directions: What answer choice should you put in the place of the question mark so that both sides of the equal sign total the same amount?

1

$$42 \quad = \quad 3 \quad x \quad \boxed{?}$$

(A) 13   (B) 42   (C) 14   (D) 12   (E) 39

2

$$7 \quad x \quad 3 \quad = \quad 39 \quad - \quad \boxed{?}$$

(A) 60   (B) 21   (C) 35   (D) 29   (E) 18

3

$$19 \quad + \quad 9 \quad = \quad 2 \quad x \quad \boxed{?}$$

(A) 28   (B) 14   (C) 26   (D) 5   (E) 4

4

$$46 \quad + \quad 34 \quad = \quad 25 \quad + \quad \boxed{?}$$

(A) 105   (B) 13   (C) 45   (D) 55   (E) 80

5

$$3 \quad + \quad \boxed{?} \quad = \quad \blacklozenge$$

$$2 \quad x \quad \blacklozenge \quad = \quad 20$$

(A) 15   (B) 7   (C) 10   (D) 3   (E) 1

6

$$9 \quad + \quad 6 \quad = \quad \boxed{?} \quad \div \quad 3$$

(A) 72   (B) 12   (C) 45   (D) 18   (E) 7

7

$$\boxed{?} \quad \div \quad 4 \quad = \quad 3 \quad x \quad 5$$

(A) 32   (B) 25   (C) 60   (D) 19   (E) 15

8

$$15 \quad + \quad 29 \quad + \quad 24 \quad = \quad 94 \quad - \quad \boxed{?}$$

(A) 36   (B) 26   (C) 68   (D) 16   (E) 75

9

$$1 \quad + \quad \boxed{?} \quad = \quad \blacklozenge$$

$$9 \quad - \quad \blacklozenge \quad = \quad 2$$

(A) 6   (B) 3   (C) 7   (D) 4   (E) 2

10

$$9 \quad x \quad 5 \quad = \quad \boxed{?} \quad + \quad 11$$

(A) 3   (B) 34   (C) 15   (D) 56   (E) 64

11

$$12 \times 3 = \boxed{?} \times 9$$

(A) 1   (B) 6   (C) 36   (D) 5   (E) 4

12

$$57 = 34 - 6 + \boxed{?}$$

(A) 17   (B) 10   (C) 30   (D) 29   (E) 28

13

$$4 + \boxed{?} = \blacklozenge$$

$$2 + \blacklozenge = 21$$

(A) 15   (B) 19   (C) 8   (D) 14   (E) 5

14

$$2 \times \boxed{?} = \blacklozenge$$

$$2 + \blacklozenge = 12$$

(A) 3   (B) 6   (C) 10   (D) 9   (E) 5

15

$$49 + 13 = \boxed{?} - 8$$

(A) 44   (B) 70   (C) 80   (D) 60   (E) 54

16

$$32 \quad - \quad 25 \quad = \quad \boxed{?} \quad \div \quad 8$$

(A) 57   (B) 15   (C) 7   (D) 56   (E) 4

17

$$\boxed{?} \quad \div \quad 7 \quad = \quad 3 \quad x \quad 4$$

(A) 49   (B) 50   (C) 84   (D) 30   (E) 6

18

$$2 \quad x \quad \boxed{?} \quad = \quad \blacklozenge$$

$$88 \quad \div \quad \blacklozenge \quad = \quad 11$$

(A) 77   (B) 6   (C) 9   (D) 8   (E) 4

19

$$\boxed{?} \quad = \quad \blacklozenge \quad + \quad 2$$

$$9 \quad = \quad \blacklozenge \quad + \quad \bullet$$

$$\bullet \quad = \quad 1$$

(A) 12   (B) 20   (C) 10   (D) 30   (E) 8

20

$$\boxed{?} \quad = \quad \blacklozenge \quad + \quad 6$$

$$5 \quad = \quad \blacklozenge \quad - \quad \bullet$$

$$\bullet \quad = \quad 2$$

(A) 5   (B) 13   (C) 7   (D) 3   (E) 4

Directions: Look at the first two sets of numbers. Come up with a rule that both sets follow. Take this rule to figure out which answer choice goes in the place of the question mark.

1   [11 → 88]   [12 → 96]   [9 → ?]

   Ⓐ 17   Ⓑ 80   Ⓒ 72   Ⓓ 90   Ⓔ 74

2   [33 → 44]   [45 → 56]   [79 → ?]

   Ⓐ 65   Ⓑ 99   Ⓒ 68   Ⓓ 88   Ⓔ 90

3   [84 → 12]   [7 → 1]   [42 → ?]

   Ⓐ 6   Ⓑ 36   Ⓒ 33   Ⓓ 72   Ⓔ 49

4   [27 → 9]   [54 → 36]   [33 → ?]

   Ⓐ 3   Ⓑ 99   Ⓒ 11   Ⓓ 15   Ⓔ 18

5   [7 → 84]   [3 → 36]   [5 → ?]

   Ⓐ 38   Ⓑ 17   Ⓒ 60   Ⓓ 82   Ⓔ 12

6   [4 → 16]   [12 → 48]   [7 → ?]

   Ⓐ 11   Ⓑ 84   Ⓒ 46   Ⓓ 28   Ⓔ 43

7   [40 → 20]   [63 → 43]   [20 → ?]

Ⓐ 1   Ⓑ 0   Ⓒ 40   Ⓓ 10   Ⓔ 20

8   [0.45 → 4.5]   [0.06 → 0.6]   [10 → ?]

Ⓐ 100   Ⓑ 1   Ⓒ 10.1   Ⓓ 10.101   Ⓔ 1.01

9   [1/2 → 3/6]   [1/4 → 2/8]   [1/2 → ?]

Ⓐ 1/6   Ⓑ 5/10   Ⓒ 1/4   Ⓓ 2/3   Ⓔ 6/10

10   [13 → 78]   [9 → 54]   [11 → ?]

Ⓐ 56   Ⓑ 5   Ⓒ 6   Ⓓ 17   Ⓔ 66

11   [3 → 12]   [51 → 60]   [18 → ?]

Ⓐ 25   Ⓑ 2   Ⓒ 9   Ⓓ 27   Ⓔ 45

12   [6 → 24]   [29 → 47]   [36 → ?]

Ⓐ 2   Ⓑ 18   Ⓒ 54   Ⓓ 44   Ⓔ 16

13   [6   →   78]   [3   →   39]   [5   →   ?]

  Ⓐ 18   Ⓑ 65   Ⓒ 41   Ⓓ 37   Ⓔ 77

14   [84   →   14]   [54   →   9]   [72   →   ?]

  Ⓐ 12   Ⓑ 66   Ⓒ 78   Ⓓ 117   Ⓔ 84

15   [21   →   7]   [62   →   48]   [30   →   ?]

  Ⓐ 10   Ⓑ 33   Ⓒ 27   Ⓓ 16   Ⓔ 30

16   [10   →   41]   [8   →   39]   [9   →   ?]

  Ⓐ 22   Ⓑ 14   Ⓒ 40   Ⓓ 30   Ⓔ 25

17   [40   →   10]   [20   →   5]   [52   →   ?]

  Ⓐ 56   Ⓑ 48   Ⓒ 13   Ⓓ 37   Ⓔ 22

18   [11   →   33]   [49   →   71]   [18   →   ?]

  Ⓐ 54   Ⓑ 40   Ⓒ 6   Ⓓ 22   Ⓔ 10

19   [12   →   108]   [6   →   54]   [9   →   ?]

    Ⓐ 57   Ⓑ 10   Ⓒ 1   Ⓓ 18   Ⓔ 81

20   [24   →   3]   [55   →   34]   [80   →   ?]

    Ⓐ 60   Ⓑ 10   Ⓒ 17   Ⓓ 59   Ⓔ 21

21   [5   →   20]   [45   →   60]   [20   →   ?]

    Ⓐ 35   Ⓑ 80   Ⓒ 5   Ⓓ 15   Ⓔ 10

22   [77   →   11]   [56   →   8]   [21   →   ?]

    Ⓐ 14   Ⓑ 28   Ⓒ 3   Ⓓ 7   Ⓔ 69

23   [96   →   12]   [64   →   8]   [32   →   ?]

    Ⓐ 6   Ⓑ 118   Ⓒ 40   Ⓓ 24   Ⓔ 4

24   [9   →   3]   [82   →   76]   [18   →   ?]

    Ⓐ 12   Ⓑ 3   Ⓒ 24   Ⓓ 54   Ⓔ 10

Directions: Which answer choice would complete the pattern?

1   **43**   **51**   **59**   **67**   **75**   **83**   **?**

     Ⓐ 91   Ⓑ 81   Ⓒ 90   Ⓓ 88   Ⓔ 86

2   **91**   **79**   **67**   **55**   **43**   **31**   **19**   **?**

     Ⓐ 39   Ⓑ 40   Ⓒ 17   Ⓓ 12   Ⓔ 7

3   **1**   **3**   **9**   **27**   **?**

     Ⓐ 24   Ⓑ 30   Ⓒ 81   Ⓓ 33   Ⓔ 35

4   **12**   **13**   **15**   **16**   **18**   **19**   **21**   **22**   **24**   **?**

     Ⓐ 19   Ⓑ 26   Ⓒ 20   Ⓓ 24   Ⓔ 25

5   **3**   **12**   **3**   **14**   **3**   **16**   **3**   **18**   **3**   **?**

     Ⓐ 20   Ⓑ 19   Ⓒ 3   Ⓓ 22   Ⓔ 4

6   **10.2**   **11.2**   **12.2**   **13.2**   **14.2**   **15.2**   **?**

Ⓐ 15.3   Ⓑ 16.2   Ⓒ 16.02   Ⓓ 16.22   Ⓔ 15.21

7   **49**   **48**   **46**   **45**   **43**   **42**   **40**   **39**   **?**

Ⓐ 41   Ⓑ 37   Ⓒ 28   Ⓓ 36   Ⓔ 38

8   **23**   **23**   **21**   **21**   **19**   **19**   **17**   **17**   **?**

Ⓐ 20   Ⓑ 13   Ⓒ 18   Ⓓ 16   Ⓔ 15

9   **40**   **39**   **37**   **34**   **30**   **25**   **19**   **12**   **?**

Ⓐ 25   Ⓑ 20   Ⓒ 6   Ⓓ 4   Ⓔ 8

10   **41**   **39**   **35**   **33**   **29**   **27**   **23**   **21**   **?**

Ⓐ 17   Ⓑ 19   Ⓒ 18   Ⓓ 20   Ⓔ 10

11   **0**   **1**   **2**   **4**   **5**   **6**   **8**   **9**   **10**   **?**

Ⓐ 8   Ⓑ 11   Ⓒ 13   Ⓓ 12   Ⓔ 14

12 **12** **5** **15** **5** **18** **5** **21** **5** **?**

Ⓐ 5   Ⓑ 4   Ⓒ 24   Ⓓ 22   Ⓔ 26

13 **35** **34** **33** **31** **30** **29** **27** **26** **25** **?**

Ⓐ 25   Ⓑ 24   Ⓒ 28   Ⓓ 23   Ⓔ 20

14 **0.4** **1.4** **2.4** **3.4** **4.4** **5.4** **6.4** **?**

Ⓐ 7.4   Ⓑ 6.5   Ⓒ 6.6   Ⓓ 7.0   Ⓔ 8.4

15 **3** **4** **10** **11** **17** **18** **24** **25** **31** **?**

Ⓐ 35   Ⓑ 29   Ⓒ 33   Ⓓ 37   Ⓔ 32

16 **40** **38** **35** **31** **26** **20** **13** **?**

Ⓐ 7   Ⓑ 6   Ⓒ 5   Ⓓ 21   Ⓔ 8

17 **50** **10** **51** **11** **52** **12** **53** **13** **54** **?**

Ⓐ 64   Ⓑ 14   Ⓒ 55   Ⓓ 15   Ⓔ 44

18   **32**   **10**   **31**   **9**   **30**   **8**   **29**   **7**   **28**   **?**

Ⓐ 5   Ⓑ 30   Ⓒ 4   Ⓓ 27   Ⓔ 6

19   **20**   **-19**   **18**   **-17**   **16**   **-15**   **14**   **-13**   **12**   **?**

Ⓐ -11   Ⓑ -10   Ⓒ 10   Ⓓ 11   Ⓔ 20

20   **1**   **12**   **6**   **17**   **11**   **22**   **16**   **?**

Ⓐ 10   Ⓑ 22   Ⓒ 27   Ⓓ 11   Ⓔ 6

21   **3**   **10**   **4**   **11**   **5**   **12**   **6**   **13**   **7**   **?**

Ⓐ 6   Ⓑ 15   Ⓒ 8   Ⓓ 14   Ⓔ 12

22   **40**   **38**   **41**   **37**   **42**   **36**   **43**   **35**   **?**

Ⓐ 40   Ⓑ 46   Ⓒ 45   Ⓓ 37   Ⓔ 44

23   **51**   **50**   **49**   **47**   **46**   **45**   **43**   **42**   **41**   **39**   **?**

Ⓐ 40   Ⓑ 39   Ⓒ 38   Ⓓ 41   Ⓔ 37

PRACTICE TEST 1 ANSWER KEY

- Compare these answers to what your child marked on the Practice Test 1 (Workbook Format) answer choices.
- At the end of each group of questions, total the number of questions answered correctly. This will provide a general overview of strengths/weaknesses according to the question type.

Verbal Classification, Practice Test 1 (Workbook Format)   Questions Answered Correctly: _____ out of 20
_____ 1. E. continents   _____ 2. B. flying insects   _____ 3. A. 3-D shapes
_____ 4. E. parts of hand   _____ 5. D. kinds of trees
_____ 6: C. names of babies   _____ 7. A. single objects naturally occurring in outer space
_____ 8. D. fruit that grows on trees   _____ 9. D. temperature adjectives
_____ 10. E. things that protect an animal by covering its skin   _____ 11. B. 4-sided shapes
_____ 12. A. kinds of plants   _____ 13. C. parts of an animal's foot
_____ 14. E. sports that can only be played with a team and with a ball
_____ 15. A. outside parts of a car   _____ 16. B. extreme weather events
_____ 17. D. things that are underground _____ 18. E. people whose job is to teach others
_____ 19. D. words having to do with going down
_____ 20. C. a means of transportation on land (note that it's not "things that begin with "t"/"tr" because there's more than one choice that has "t"/"tr" as the first letters)

Verbal Analogies, Practice Test 1 (Workbook Format)   Questions Answered Correctly: _____ out of 22
_____ 1. C. Afternoon is the time of day before night. Fall is the season before winter.
_____ 2. B. You sweep with a broom. You weigh with a scale. (The first word is the activity done with the second word.)
_____ 3. C. same kind (oceans/continents)
_____ 4. D. Soap is used to clean hands and rinsed away with water. Toothpaste is used to clean teeth and rinsed away with water.
_____ 5. B. A cyclist rides on a bicycle. A surfer rides on a board. (Note that it's not wave or ocean because the surfer is actually on the board like a cyclist is on a bicycle.)
_____ 6. A. same animal class (reptiles/mammals)   _____ 7. D. A diamond is a type of gem. Silver is a type of metal.
_____ 8. A. In the winter, ducks migrate and bears hibernate.
_____ 9. D. A cello is a type of instrument. A cactus is a type of plant.
_____ 10. B. A team is made up of players. A month is made up of weeks.
_____ 11. C. A helmet is worn over your head. A seatbelt is worn over your waist (and your chest).
_____ 12. E. animal > animal's sound
_____ 13. A. A waiter works at a restaurant. A nurse works at a hospital.
_____ 14. C. A captain is in charge of (or leads) a boat. A mayor is in charge of (or leads) a city.
_____ 15. A. opposites
_____ 16. D. It's a singer's job to perform (sing) in a concert. It's an actress' job to perform (act) in a movie.
_____ 17. E. habitat > mammal found in this habitat   _____ 18. A. singular > plural
_____ 19. E. A poet puts words together to create poems. A chef puts ingredients together to create meals.
_____ 20. B. Elated means very happy. Drenched means very wet.
_____ 21. A. object > part that's underground   _____ 22. E. opposites

Sentence Completion, Practice Test 1 (Workbook Format)   Questions Answered Correctly: _____ out of 20
_____ 1. C. combine: to mix together   _____ 2. A. rival: a competitor
_____ 3. B. decrease: to become less
_____ 4. A. prescribe: to tell somebody to use a medicine and usually write something for the medicine to be bought at a pharmacy
_____ 5. E. prevent: to stop something from happening
_____ 6. A. the word tested here is actually "lack"; lack: to not have something
_____ 7. C. inflate: to add air to something which makes it larger; prior: before
_____ 8. D. strategy: a careful plan to reach a goal   _____ 9. B. insist: to say that something must happen
_____ 10. C. simplify: to make something more simple   _____ 11. A. drastic: severe or harsh
_____ 12. B. vital: very, very important   _____ 13. E. essential: necessary
_____ 14. D. evaluate: to form an idea about and judge something
_____ 15. B. recount: to count again   _____ 16. A. diminish: to become less
_____ 17. B. anticipate: to expect or predict   _____ 18. C. concise: giving information in a short, clear way
_____ 19. E. discontinue: to not continue, to stop; irritate: to bother
_____ 20. A. variable: changing

Figure Classification, Practice Test 1 (Workbook Format)   Questions Answered Correctly: _____ out of 22
_____ 1. A.
_____ 2. B. the 2 shapes are different kinds of shapes & their inside design is different: 1 is gray, 1 is filled with wavy lines
_____ 3. A. triangles pointing right   _____ 4. E. group of 3 shapes: 2 gray shapes, 1 black shape
_____ 5. C. 1 black heart, 1 gray rectangle, 1 oval filled with lines
_____ 6. E. 2 overlapping shapes that are not flipped, and where all of the lines are seen
_____ 7. B. 1 gray "pac-man," 1 gray hexagon, 1 black oval, 1 white star
_____ 8. D. 2 gray circles that are adjacent to the middle gray circle with none of the gray circles directly next to each other

_____ 9. A. half of shape is gray/half is white
_____ 10. E. shapes are divided in half
_____ 11. D. shapes filled in wavy lines
_____ 12. E. the shape rotates 90 degrees counterclockwise
_____ 13. C. shapes have at least 2 rounded corners
_____ 14. B. each oval has: 1 heart, 1 trapezoid, 1 square
_____ 15. D. middle shape has diagonal lines
_____ 16. B. pentagon with dashed lines
_____ 17. D. the straight line of the gray semi-circle is on the edge of the larger shape
_____ 18. A. smaller inner shape has 1 less side than larger outer shape
_____ 19. B. smaller inner shapes are a different color than the larger square; the smaller inner shapes are: 1 rectangle, 1 oval, 1 trapezoid
_____ 20. D. 2 smaller shapes are smaller versions of the larger shape divided in half
_____ 21. E. inside oval are a triangle and square that are directly beside each other
_____ 22. E. inside triangle are: 1 black shape, 1 gray shape, 1 white shape

Figure Analogies, Practice Test 1 (Workbook Format)   Questions Answered Correctly: _____ out of 22

_____ 1. D.
_____ 2. E. the larger shape becomes the color of the smaller shape & the larger shape is by itself
_____ 3. B. the black shape has the same amount of sides as the arrow points in the first box
_____ 4. C. black changes to gray, gray changes to black
_____ 5. B. larger & smaller shapes switch colors
_____ 6. D. gray shape rotates 90 degrees clockwise & a rectangle is added bordering it
_____ 7. A. shapes rotate 180 degrees & reverse color (if octagons rotate, you do not notice it, but with trapezoids you do)
_____ 8. A. same group of larger shapes has group of small gray shapes (aligned horizontally) added to middle
_____ 9. C. rotates 90 degrees clockwise (to the right)
_____ 10. E. designs inside 4 squares change like this: gray becomes vertical lines & vice versa; black becomes dotted lines & vice versa
_____ 11. B. black shape becomes gray & adds one more side; gray shape becomes black & adds one more side
_____ 12. C. octagon becomes hexagon, white sections become gray, gray sections become white, dotted sections remain the same
_____ 13. D. circle becomes oval & rectangle rotates 180 degrees
_____ 14. A. shapes change from hearts to triangles & there's 1 less smaller shape
_____ 15. C. shape group rotates 180 degrees; gray & black colors switch
_____ 16. D. gray shapes become black, black shapes become gray; smallest center shape & outer shape switch positions; middle shapes (star on top & parallelogram on bottom) get bigger
_____ 17. E. shape group rotates 90 degrees clockwise, then shape colors gray/white switch
_____ 18. D. smaller shape moves inside the larger shape, then this smaller shape rotates 90 degrees & then a mirror image of this shape appears next to it
_____ 19. A. second shape group is a "flip"/mirror image of the first
_____ 20. E. shape group rotates 180 degrees
_____ 21. B. designs change like this: crescents facing right become black stars; crescents facing up become white stars; crescents facing down become "M"
_____ 22. D. shape group is a "flip"/mirror image of the first; in the center shape, white becomes dotted & vice versa; the left half of the center shape is covered

Paper Folding Practice Test 1 (Workbook Format)   Questions Answered Correctly: _____ out of 17

_____ 1. E	_____ 2. A	_____ 3. B	_____ 4. D	_____ 5. C	_____ 6. C	_____ 7. C
_____ 8. A	_____ 9. B	_____ 10. C	_____ 11. E	_____ 12. A	_____ 13. D	_____ 14. E
_____ 15. B	_____ 16. A	_____ 17. E				

Number Puzzles Practice Test 1 (Workbook Format)   Questions Correctly: _____ out of 17

_____ 1. C	_____ 2. A	_____ 3. E	_____ 4. C	_____ 5. C	_____ 6. B	_____ 7. B	_____ 8. D
_____ 9. A	_____ 10. C	_____ 11. E	_____ 12. C	_____ 13. B	_____ 14. D	_____ 15. A	
_____ 16. D	_____ 17. E						

Number Analogies Practice Test 1 (Workbook Format)   Questions Correctly: _____ out of 23

_____ 1. B. +8	_____ 2. E. -5	_____ 3. C. ÷2	_____ 4. E. x5	_____ 5. C. x2
_____ 6. B. ÷3	_____ 7. D. -30	_____ 8. A. ÷2	_____ 9. B. same	_____ 10. E. x10
_____ 11. E. +15	_____ 12. C. x2	_____ 13. B. ÷4	_____ 14. D. x12	_____ 15. D. x4
_____ 16. C. -9	_____ 17. C. +13	_____ 18. B. x20	_____ 19. E. x7	_____ 20. D. ÷8
_____ 21. A. -23	_____ 22. C. ÷6	_____ 23. B. ÷9		

continued on the next page

Number Series, Practice Test 1 (Workbook Format)   Questions Answered Correctly: _____ out of 23
_____ 1. D. -5   _____ 2. E. +18
_____ 3. D. x2 previous number
_____ 4. B. +1, +2, +1, +2, continues -OR- with every other number there's a difference of +3 (i.e., 3, 6, 9, etc. & 4, 7, 10, etc.)
_____ 5. C. -1, -2, -1, -2, continues -OR- with every other number there's a difference of -3
_____ 6. C. +1
_____ 7. A. begins w/1, every other number is 1; then, starting with 20, every other number is +1
_____ 8. B. every number repeats itself and then decreases by 2
_____ 9. E. +1, +5, +1, +5, continues -OR- with every other number there's a difference of +6
_____ 10. C. -2, -4, -2, -4, continues -OR- with every other number there's a difference of -6
_____ 11. D. +1, +1, +2; +1, +1, +2, continues   _____ 12. A. -1, -1, -2; -1, -1, -2, continues
_____ 13. C. begins w/3, every other number is 3; then, starting with 10, every other number is +5
_____ 14. A. +1   _____ 15. D. -1, -2, -3, -4, -5, etc.
_____ 16. B. +2, +3, +4, +5, +6, etc.
_____ 17. E. the numbers in spaces 1, 3, 5, 7, 9 increase by 1; the numbers in spaces 2, 4, 6, 8, 10 increase by 1 -OR-
+9, -8, +9, -8, etc.
_____ 18. B. the numbers in spaces 1, 3, 5, 7, 9 decrease by 1; the numbers in spaces 2, 4, 6, 8, 10 increase by 1 -OR-
-17, +16, -15, +14 (here, the two digits decrease by 1 & the math operation alternates between subtraction and addition)
_____ 19. D. the digits decrease by 1 (i.e., from 10 to 9 to 8 to 7) -AND- the signs alternate between positive and negative -OR-
the numbers in spaces 1, 3, 5, 7 decrease by 2; the numbers in spaces 2, 4, 6, 8 increase by 2
_____ 20. E. -10, +4, etc. -OR- with every other number there's a difference of -6
_____ 21. A. the numbers in spaces 1, 3, 5, 7, 9 increase by 1; the numbers in spaces 2, 4, 6, 8, 10 increase by 1 -OR-
+6, -5, +6, -5, etc.
_____ 22. B. the numbers in spaces 1, 3, 5, 7, 9 increase by 1; the numbers in spaces 2, 4, 6, 8, 10 decrease by 1 -OR-
+13, -12, +11, -10, +9 (here, the two digits decrease by 1 & the math operation alternates between subtraction and addition)
_____ 23. C. +1, +1, +2; +1, +1, +2, etc.

PRACTICE TEST 2 ANSWER KEY

- Compare these answers to what your child marked on the Practice Test 2 bubble sheet.
- At the end of each group of questions, total the number of questions answered correctly. This will provide a general overview of strengths/weaknesses according to the question type.

Verbal Classification, Practice Test 2   Questions Answered Correctly: _____ out of 20
_____ 1. B. birds   _____ 2. E. come in pairs   _____ 3. A. things that hold liquid
_____ 4. C. things that are green   _____ 5. B. animals with 4 legs   _____ 6. C. units of measurement
_____ 7. D. things you climb   _____ 8. A. kinds of seats   _____ 9. B. places where cars travel
_____ 10. C. professions involved in building   _____ 11. D. food that grows under the ground
_____ 12. A. adjectives having to do with happiness and festivity   _____ 13. B. stringed instruments
_____ 14. E. adjectives used to describe frequency
_____ 15. D. adjectives having to do with size   _____ 16. E. types of leaders
_____ 17. B. words having to do with moving things from one place to another
_____ 18. C. places that are at the top
_____ 19. A. naturally occurring bodies of water (canal is man-made)   _____ 20. E. types of fictional stories

Verbal Analogies, Practice Test 2   Questions Answered Correctly: _____ out of 22
_____ 1. E. opposites   _____ 2. B. Hours make up a day. Days make up a month.
_____ 3. A. Tuna is a type of fish. Pine is a type of tree.
_____ 4. D. A ship carries cargo, transporting it from one place to another. A subway does this with passengers. (Note that it's not
conductor because the subway's function is to carry passengers, not conductors.)
_____ 5. C. A novel is made up of chapters put together. A play is made up of scenes put together.
_____ 6. B. A tricycle has 3 wheels. A triangle has 3 sides.   _____ 7. E. opposites
_____ 8. B. A cover is on the outside of a book to protect it and give an idea about what's inside in the same way that an
envelope is with a letter.
_____ 9. A. A bird is covered in many feathers. A fish is covered in many scales.
_____ 10. B. A field is where corn typically grows for harvest. An orchard is where apples are grown for harvest.
_____ 11. A. Clay is used to make pottery; pottery comes from clay. Sand is used to make glass; glass comes from sand.
_____ 12. D. A herd is the name of a group of buffalo. A pack is the name of a group of wolves.
_____ 13. B. Twelve things equals a dozen. Twelve inches equals a foot.
_____ 14. E. A refrigerator runs on electricity. A watch runs on a battery.   _____ 15. A. animal > animal's movement
_____ 16. A. A group of musicians working together is a band. A group of sailors working together is a crew.
_____ 17. B. It takes 100 cents to make a dollar and 100 years to make a century.
_____ 18. C. A judge decides penalties and makes rulings in a court case. A referee does this in basketball games.
_____ 19. B. synonyms
_____ 20. A. Paddles make a kayak move. Sails make a yacht move.
_____ 21. D. Something without enough water is dry. Something without enough light is dim.
_____ 22. E. opposites

Sentence Completion, Practice Test 2
Questions Answered Correctly: _____ out of 20

_____ 1. C. precise: exact   _____ 2. E. mimic: to copy   _____ 3. A. support: to hold up
_____ 4. B. abundant: a lot/a large quantity
_____ 5. D. rarely: hardly ever; disobey: to not obey, to not follow directions   _____ 6. D. arid: dry; not having much rain
_____ 7. C. conserving/to conserve: to save and use carefully
_____ 8. A. gained/to gain: to get something or win something   _____ 9. B. continuous: not stopping
_____ 10. E. extreme: very, very far away from what is thought to be the usual or the middle
_____ 11. D. specific: exact   _____ 12. B. realistic: based on what is real
_____ 13. D. expedition: a journey with a purpose   _____ 14. A. irregular: not regular
_____ 15. B. ample: a lot of   _____ 16. A. beneficial: causing benefits/good results
_____ 17. C. improbable: not probable, not likely   _____ 18. E. massive: extremely large
_____ 19. A. unlimited: without a limit   _____ 20. E. destructive: causing destruction/damage

Figure Classification, Practice Test 2
Questions Answered Correctly: _____ out of 22

_____ 1. E. 4-sided shapes
_____ 2. D. as figure rotates, the gray shape remains at the same spot on the larger black shape
_____ 3. C. line dividing shape goes from upper left to lower right
_____ 4. A. 4-sided shapes that have different designs/colors in the smaller and larger shapes
_____ 5. D. 7-sided shapes   _____ 6. C. 3-D shapes   _____ 7. B. diamonds
_____ 8. D. 2 lines (and only 2 lines) cross inside shape   _____ 9. C. bottom shape rotates 90 degrees counterclockwise
_____ 10. C. inner & outer shapes have different colors/designs inside
_____ 11. D. shapes are equilateral
_____ 12. A. there are 3 shapes: 1 oval, 1 trapezoid, 1 cube; each shape is either: white, black, or filled with dots
_____ 13. E. larger shape is divided and part is filled with dots and part is white; there is a small, white version of the larger shape that's inside the white section
_____ 14. E. each shape group has: 1 hexagon, 1 square, 1 heart; each shape is either: black, gray, or filled with diagonal lines
_____ 15. A. inner shape has 1 more side than outer shape
_____ 16. D. the 2 crossed lines inside the shape are shaped like an "X"
_____ 17. B. tic-tac-toe formed by the hearts and there is only 1 other shape which is a star
_____ 18. A. inside the square are 2 different shapes and 1 shape is black, 1 is white
_____ 19. C. larger shape is a trapezoid & a smaller, different colored shape is in the upper right corner
_____ 20. C. the largest & smallest shapes have the same color/design inside & the 3 shapes are different kinds of shapes
_____ 21. D. inside the largest shape the diagonal lines go from lower left to upper right
_____ 22. B. shape group is aligned diagonally and must have 1 of each shape (diamond, pentagon, heart) and 1 of each color/design (dotted, gray, black)

Figure Analogies, Practice Test 2
Questions Answered Correctly: _____ out of 22

_____ 1. C. gray shape in middle becomes white; white shape in middle becomes gray; another larger white version of this shape is added around the smaller shape
_____ 2. B. the shape on the right side is the same shape made by the thin rectangles in the left side
_____ 3. E. top half of the shape group is showing
_____ 4. C. arch shape rotates 180 degrees & the colors of the small shapes switch
_____ 5. E. inner shape gets larger/wider & outer shape gets smaller/narrower, turns gray, and moves inside
_____ 6. A. bottom shape rotates 180 degrees & top shape moves down; in the group, white shapes change from being white to being filled with dots & shapes filled with dots turn white
_____ 7. D. white sections become black & sections filled with lines become white
_____ 8. D. squares become stars & vice versa; circles become triangles & vice versa
_____ 9. E. half the number of shapes from the original group & these shapes do not have any diagonal lines
_____ 10. A. the divided shapes change the designs of their sections like this: gray become horizontal lines, dotted become gray, horizontal lines become dotted
_____ 11. D. gray shapes become black, black shapes become gray; larger outer shape & smallest inner shape switch positions; middle shape becomes smaller
_____ 12. C. white shape rotates 90 degrees counterclockwise & gray shape is removed
_____ 13. E. shapes inside circle change: top left shape rotates 180 degrees, bottom right & top right shapes switch position
_____ 14. D. shape group rotates 90 degrees clockwise & shapes reverse color
_____ 15. E. bottom shape gets bigger, top shape gets bigger and moves inside the bottom shape, middle shape moves to the center of this shape group, the middle shape also rotates 90 degrees clockwise
_____ 16. B. the shape that was "behind" the front shape is now at the front (on top it was the star that moved to the front, on bottom the circle moved to the front), this shape turns black; the shape that was originally in front moves to the back and turns gray; then, the shape group rotates 90 degrees counterclockwise
_____ 17. C. shapes change from diamonds to hexagons & the striped sections alternate positions (top left -> top right & vice versa; bottom left -> bottom right & vice versa)
_____ 18. B. shape rotates 90 degrees counterclockwise & a circle is added
_____ 19. E. shapes inside the square change like this: triangles become circles & circles become triangles; stars stay the same
_____ 20. B. patterns inside circle change like this: dots become horizontal lines & vice versa; gray stays the same
_____ 21. A. original shape "flips" down/becomes a mirror image & another shape identical to the first one is added on top, but then turns gray
_____ 22. D. in the larger shape, a shape with one more side than this larger shape is in each of the corners

Paper Folding, Practice Test 2

Questions Answered Correctly: _____ out of 15

_____ 1. D   _____ 2. C   _____ 3. C   _____ 4. B   _____ 5. A   _____ 6. E   _____ 7. A   _____ 8. D
_____ 9. C   _____ 10. B   _____ 11. A   _____ 12. C   _____ 13. E   _____ 14. D   _____ 15. A

Number Puzzles, Practice Test 2

Questions Answered Correctly: _____ out of 20

_____ 1. C   _____ 2. E   _____ 3. B   _____ 4. D   _____ 5. B   _____ 6. C   _____ 7. C   _____ 8. B
_____ 9. A   _____ 10. B   _____ 11. E   _____ 12. D   _____ 13. A   _____ 14. E   _____ 15. B   _____ 16. D
_____ 17. C   _____ 18. E   _____ 19. C   _____ 20. B

Number Analogies, Practice Test 2

Questions Answered Correctly: _____ out of 24

_____ 1. C. x 8   _____ 2. E. +11   _____ 3. A. ÷ 7   _____ 4. D. -18   _____ 5. C. x 12
_____ 6. D. x 4   _____ 7. B. -20   _____ 8. A. x 10   _____ 9. B. same   _____ 10. E. x 6
_____ 11. D. + 9   _____ 12. C. + 18   _____ 13. B. x 13   _____ 14. A. ÷ 6   _____ 15. D. -14
_____ 16. C. +31   _____ 17. C. ÷ 4   _____ 18. B. +22   _____ 19. E. x 9   _____ 20. D. -21
_____ 21. A. +15   _____ 22. C. ÷ 7   _____ 23. E. ÷ 8   _____ 24. A. - 6

Number Series, Practice Test 2

Questions Answered Correctly: _____ out of 23

_____ 1. A. +8   _____ 2. E. -12   _____ 3. C. x3

_____ 4. E. +1, +2, +1, +2, continues -OR- with every other number there is a difference of +3 (i.e., between 12, 15, 18, etc. & 13, 16, 19, etc.)

_____ 5. A. begins w/3, every other number is 3; then, starting with 12, every other number is +2

_____ 6. B. +1

_____ 7. B. -1, -2, -1, -2, continues -OR- with every other number there is a difference of -3 (i.e., between 49, 46, 43, etc. & 48, 45, 42, etc.)

_____ 8. E. every number repeats itself and then decreases by 2   _____ 9. D. -1, -2, -3, -4, -5, etc.

_____ 10. A. -2, -4, -2, -4, continues -OR- with every other number there is a difference of -6

_____ 11. D. +1, +1, +2; +1, +1, +2, continues

_____ 12. C. starting with 12, every other number is +3; the other numbers in between these are "5"

_____ 13. D. -1, -1, -2; -1, -1, -2, continues   _____ 14. A. +1

_____ 15. E. +1, +6, +1, +6, continues -OR- with every other number there is a difference of +7

_____ 16. C. -2, -3, -4, -5, -6, etc.

_____ 17. B. the numbers in spaces 1, 3, 5, 7, 9 increase by 1; the numbers in spaces 2, 4, 6, 8, 10 increase by 1 -OR- with each pair of numbers (50 & 10, 51 & 11, 52 & 12, etc., there is a difference of 40)

_____ 18. E. the numbers in spaces 1, 3, 5, 7, 9 decrease by 1; the numbers in spaces 2, 4, 6, 8, 10 decrease by 1 -OR- with each pair of numbers (32 & 10, 31 & 9, etc., there is a difference of 22)

_____ 19. A. the digits decrease by 1 (i.e., from 20 to 19 to 18 to 17, etc.) -AND- the numbers alternate between positive and negative

_____ 20. C. +11,-6, etc. -OR- with every other number there is a difference of +5

_____ 21. D. the numbers in spaces 1, 3, 5, 7, 9 increase by 1; the numbers in spaces 2, 4, 6, 8, 10 increase by 1 -OR- +7, -6, +7, -6, etc.

_____ 22. E. the numbers in spaces 1, 3, 5, 7, 9 increase by 1; the numbers in spaces 2, 4, 6, 8 decrease by 1 -OR- -2, +3, -4, +5, -6

_____ 23. C. -1, -1, -2; -1, -1, -2, etc.

BUBBLE SHEET FOR PRACTICE TEST 2

- Our suggestion: have your student complete Practice Test 2 on his/her own (do not tell whether the answers are correct until the test is completed).

- The time limit for each of the 9 question sections (Verbal Analogies, Verbal Classification, etc.) is approximately 15 minutes each.

Our suggestion: do a group of 3 question sections per day.

- Day 1, Verbal: 15 minutes each for Verbal Analogies, Verbal Classification, Sentence Completion = 45 minutes total
- Day 2, Non-Verbal: 15 minutes each for Figure Analogies, Figure Classification, Paper Folding = 45 minutes total
- Day 3, Quantitative: 15 minutes each for Number Analogies, Number Puzzles, Number Series = 45 minutes total
- After your student is finished, on your own (without your child), go through the answer key by question type to see which answers were correct/incorrect.

Verbal Classification	Verbal Analogies	Sentence Completion	Figure Classification
1 Ⓐ Ⓑ Ⓒ Ⓓ Ⓔ	1 Ⓐ Ⓑ Ⓒ Ⓓ Ⓔ	1 Ⓐ Ⓑ Ⓒ Ⓓ Ⓔ	1 Ⓐ Ⓑ Ⓒ Ⓓ Ⓔ
2 Ⓐ Ⓑ Ⓒ Ⓓ Ⓔ	2 Ⓐ Ⓑ Ⓒ Ⓓ Ⓔ	2 Ⓐ Ⓑ Ⓒ Ⓓ Ⓔ	2 Ⓐ Ⓑ Ⓒ Ⓓ Ⓔ
3 Ⓐ Ⓑ Ⓒ Ⓓ Ⓔ	3 Ⓐ Ⓑ Ⓒ Ⓓ Ⓔ	3 Ⓐ Ⓑ Ⓒ Ⓓ Ⓔ	3 Ⓐ Ⓑ Ⓒ Ⓓ Ⓔ
4 Ⓐ Ⓑ Ⓒ Ⓓ Ⓔ	4 Ⓐ Ⓑ Ⓒ Ⓓ Ⓔ	4 Ⓐ Ⓑ Ⓒ Ⓓ Ⓔ	4 Ⓐ Ⓑ Ⓒ Ⓓ Ⓔ
5 Ⓐ Ⓑ Ⓒ Ⓓ Ⓔ	5 Ⓐ Ⓑ Ⓒ Ⓓ Ⓔ	5 Ⓐ Ⓑ Ⓒ Ⓓ Ⓔ	5 Ⓐ Ⓑ Ⓒ Ⓓ Ⓔ
6 Ⓐ Ⓑ Ⓒ Ⓓ Ⓔ	6 Ⓐ Ⓑ Ⓒ Ⓓ Ⓔ	6 Ⓐ Ⓑ Ⓒ Ⓓ Ⓔ	6 Ⓐ Ⓑ Ⓒ Ⓓ Ⓔ
7 Ⓐ Ⓑ Ⓒ Ⓓ Ⓔ	7 Ⓐ Ⓑ Ⓒ Ⓓ Ⓔ	7 Ⓐ Ⓑ Ⓒ Ⓓ Ⓔ	7 Ⓐ Ⓑ Ⓒ Ⓓ Ⓔ
8 Ⓐ Ⓑ Ⓒ Ⓓ Ⓔ	8 Ⓐ Ⓑ Ⓒ Ⓓ Ⓔ	8 Ⓐ Ⓑ Ⓒ Ⓓ Ⓔ	8 Ⓐ Ⓑ Ⓒ Ⓓ Ⓔ
9 Ⓐ Ⓑ Ⓒ Ⓓ Ⓔ	9 Ⓐ Ⓑ Ⓒ Ⓓ Ⓔ	9 Ⓐ Ⓑ Ⓒ Ⓓ Ⓔ	9 Ⓐ Ⓑ Ⓒ Ⓓ Ⓔ
10 Ⓐ Ⓑ Ⓒ Ⓓ Ⓔ	10 Ⓐ Ⓑ Ⓒ Ⓓ Ⓔ	10 Ⓐ Ⓑ Ⓒ Ⓓ Ⓔ	10 Ⓐ Ⓑ Ⓒ Ⓓ Ⓔ
11 Ⓐ Ⓑ Ⓒ Ⓓ Ⓔ	11 Ⓐ Ⓑ Ⓒ Ⓓ Ⓔ	11 Ⓐ Ⓑ Ⓒ Ⓓ Ⓔ	11 Ⓐ Ⓑ Ⓒ Ⓓ Ⓔ
12 Ⓐ Ⓑ Ⓒ Ⓓ Ⓔ	12 Ⓐ Ⓑ Ⓒ Ⓓ Ⓔ	12 Ⓐ Ⓑ Ⓒ Ⓓ Ⓔ	12 Ⓐ Ⓑ Ⓒ Ⓓ Ⓔ
13 Ⓐ Ⓑ Ⓒ Ⓓ Ⓔ	13 Ⓐ Ⓑ Ⓒ Ⓓ Ⓔ	13 Ⓐ Ⓑ Ⓒ Ⓓ Ⓔ	13 Ⓐ Ⓑ Ⓒ Ⓓ Ⓔ
14 Ⓐ Ⓑ Ⓒ Ⓓ Ⓔ	14 Ⓐ Ⓑ Ⓒ Ⓓ Ⓔ	14 Ⓐ Ⓑ Ⓒ Ⓓ Ⓔ	14 Ⓐ Ⓑ Ⓒ Ⓓ Ⓔ
15 Ⓐ Ⓑ Ⓒ Ⓓ Ⓔ	15 Ⓐ Ⓑ Ⓒ Ⓓ Ⓔ	15 Ⓐ Ⓑ Ⓒ Ⓓ Ⓔ	15 Ⓐ Ⓑ Ⓒ Ⓓ Ⓔ
16 Ⓐ Ⓑ Ⓒ Ⓓ Ⓔ	16 Ⓐ Ⓑ Ⓒ Ⓓ Ⓔ	16 Ⓐ Ⓑ Ⓒ Ⓓ Ⓔ	16 Ⓐ Ⓑ Ⓒ Ⓓ Ⓔ
17 Ⓐ Ⓑ Ⓒ Ⓓ Ⓔ	17 Ⓐ Ⓑ Ⓒ Ⓓ Ⓔ	17 Ⓐ Ⓑ Ⓒ Ⓓ Ⓔ	17 Ⓐ Ⓑ Ⓒ Ⓓ Ⓔ
18 Ⓐ Ⓑ Ⓒ Ⓓ Ⓔ	18 Ⓐ Ⓑ Ⓒ Ⓓ Ⓔ	18 Ⓐ Ⓑ Ⓒ Ⓓ Ⓔ	18 Ⓐ Ⓑ Ⓒ Ⓓ Ⓔ
19 Ⓐ Ⓑ Ⓒ Ⓓ Ⓔ	19 Ⓐ Ⓑ Ⓒ Ⓓ Ⓔ	19 Ⓐ Ⓑ Ⓒ Ⓓ Ⓔ	19 Ⓐ Ⓑ Ⓒ Ⓓ Ⓔ
20 Ⓐ Ⓑ Ⓒ Ⓓ Ⓔ	20 Ⓐ Ⓑ Ⓒ Ⓓ Ⓔ	20 Ⓐ Ⓑ Ⓒ Ⓓ Ⓔ	20 Ⓐ Ⓑ Ⓒ Ⓓ Ⓔ
	21 Ⓐ Ⓑ Ⓒ Ⓓ Ⓔ		21 Ⓐ Ⓑ Ⓒ Ⓓ Ⓔ
	22 Ⓐ Ⓑ Ⓒ Ⓓ Ⓔ		22 Ⓐ Ⓑ Ⓒ Ⓓ Ⓔ

Figure Analogies	Paper Folding	Number Puzzles	Number Analogies	Number Series
1 Ⓐ Ⓑ Ⓒ Ⓓ Ⓔ	1 Ⓐ Ⓑ Ⓒ Ⓓ Ⓔ	1 Ⓐ Ⓑ Ⓒ Ⓓ Ⓔ	1 Ⓐ Ⓑ Ⓒ Ⓓ Ⓔ	1 Ⓐ Ⓑ Ⓒ Ⓓ Ⓔ
2 Ⓐ Ⓑ Ⓒ Ⓓ Ⓔ	2 Ⓐ Ⓑ Ⓒ Ⓓ Ⓔ	2 Ⓐ Ⓑ Ⓒ Ⓓ Ⓔ	2 Ⓐ Ⓑ Ⓒ Ⓓ Ⓔ	2 Ⓐ Ⓑ Ⓒ Ⓓ Ⓔ
3 Ⓐ Ⓑ Ⓒ Ⓓ Ⓔ	3 Ⓐ Ⓑ Ⓒ Ⓓ Ⓔ	3 Ⓐ Ⓑ Ⓒ Ⓓ Ⓔ	3 Ⓐ Ⓑ Ⓒ Ⓓ Ⓔ	3 Ⓐ Ⓑ Ⓒ Ⓓ Ⓔ
4 Ⓐ Ⓑ Ⓒ Ⓓ Ⓔ	4 Ⓐ Ⓑ Ⓒ Ⓓ Ⓔ	4 Ⓐ Ⓑ Ⓒ Ⓓ Ⓔ	4 Ⓐ Ⓑ Ⓒ Ⓓ Ⓔ	4 Ⓐ Ⓑ Ⓒ Ⓓ Ⓔ
5 Ⓐ Ⓑ Ⓒ Ⓓ Ⓔ	5 Ⓐ Ⓑ Ⓒ Ⓓ Ⓔ	5 Ⓐ Ⓑ Ⓒ Ⓓ Ⓔ	5 Ⓐ Ⓑ Ⓒ Ⓓ Ⓔ	5 Ⓐ Ⓑ Ⓒ Ⓓ Ⓔ
6 Ⓐ Ⓑ Ⓒ Ⓓ Ⓔ	6 Ⓐ Ⓑ Ⓒ Ⓓ Ⓔ	6 Ⓐ Ⓑ Ⓒ Ⓓ Ⓔ	6 Ⓐ Ⓑ Ⓒ Ⓓ Ⓔ	6 Ⓐ Ⓑ Ⓒ Ⓓ Ⓔ
7 Ⓐ Ⓑ Ⓒ Ⓓ Ⓔ	7 Ⓐ Ⓑ Ⓒ Ⓓ Ⓔ	7 Ⓐ Ⓑ Ⓒ Ⓓ Ⓔ	7 Ⓐ Ⓑ Ⓒ Ⓓ Ⓔ	7 Ⓐ Ⓑ Ⓒ Ⓓ Ⓔ
8 Ⓐ Ⓑ Ⓒ Ⓓ Ⓔ	8 Ⓐ Ⓑ Ⓒ Ⓓ Ⓔ	8 Ⓐ Ⓑ Ⓒ Ⓓ Ⓔ	8 Ⓐ Ⓑ Ⓒ Ⓓ Ⓔ	8 Ⓐ Ⓑ Ⓒ Ⓓ Ⓔ
9 Ⓐ Ⓑ Ⓒ Ⓓ Ⓔ	9 Ⓐ Ⓑ Ⓒ Ⓓ Ⓔ	9 Ⓐ Ⓑ Ⓒ Ⓓ Ⓔ	9 Ⓐ Ⓑ Ⓒ Ⓓ Ⓔ	9 Ⓐ Ⓑ Ⓒ Ⓓ Ⓔ
10 Ⓐ Ⓑ Ⓒ Ⓓ Ⓔ	10 Ⓐ Ⓑ Ⓒ Ⓓ Ⓔ	10 Ⓐ Ⓑ Ⓒ Ⓓ Ⓔ	10 Ⓐ Ⓑ Ⓒ Ⓓ Ⓔ	10 Ⓐ Ⓑ Ⓒ Ⓓ Ⓔ
11 Ⓐ Ⓑ Ⓒ Ⓓ Ⓔ	11 Ⓐ Ⓑ Ⓒ Ⓓ Ⓔ	11 Ⓐ Ⓑ Ⓒ Ⓓ Ⓔ	11 Ⓐ Ⓑ Ⓒ Ⓓ Ⓔ	11 Ⓐ Ⓑ Ⓒ Ⓓ Ⓔ
12 Ⓐ Ⓑ Ⓒ Ⓓ Ⓔ	12 Ⓐ Ⓑ Ⓒ Ⓓ Ⓔ	12 Ⓐ Ⓑ Ⓒ Ⓓ Ⓔ	12 Ⓐ Ⓑ Ⓒ Ⓓ Ⓔ	12 Ⓐ Ⓑ Ⓒ Ⓓ Ⓔ
13 Ⓐ Ⓑ Ⓒ Ⓓ Ⓔ	13 Ⓐ Ⓑ Ⓒ Ⓓ Ⓔ	13 Ⓐ Ⓑ Ⓒ Ⓓ Ⓔ	13 Ⓐ Ⓑ Ⓒ Ⓓ Ⓔ	13 Ⓐ Ⓑ Ⓒ Ⓓ Ⓔ
14 Ⓐ Ⓑ Ⓒ Ⓓ Ⓔ	14 Ⓐ Ⓑ Ⓒ Ⓓ Ⓔ	14 Ⓐ Ⓑ Ⓒ Ⓓ Ⓔ	14 Ⓐ Ⓑ Ⓒ Ⓓ Ⓔ	14 Ⓐ Ⓑ Ⓒ Ⓓ Ⓔ
15 Ⓐ Ⓑ Ⓒ Ⓓ Ⓔ	15 Ⓐ Ⓑ Ⓒ Ⓓ Ⓔ	15 Ⓐ Ⓑ Ⓒ Ⓓ Ⓔ	15 Ⓐ Ⓑ Ⓒ Ⓓ Ⓔ	15 Ⓐ Ⓑ Ⓒ Ⓓ Ⓔ
16 Ⓐ Ⓑ Ⓒ Ⓓ Ⓔ		16 Ⓐ Ⓑ Ⓒ Ⓓ Ⓔ	16 Ⓐ Ⓑ Ⓒ Ⓓ Ⓔ	16 Ⓐ Ⓑ Ⓒ Ⓓ Ⓔ
17 Ⓐ Ⓑ Ⓒ Ⓓ Ⓔ		17 Ⓐ Ⓑ Ⓒ Ⓓ Ⓔ	17 Ⓐ Ⓑ Ⓒ Ⓓ Ⓔ	17 Ⓐ Ⓑ Ⓒ Ⓓ Ⓔ
18 Ⓐ Ⓑ Ⓒ Ⓓ Ⓔ		18 Ⓐ Ⓑ Ⓒ Ⓓ Ⓔ	18 Ⓐ Ⓑ Ⓒ Ⓓ Ⓔ	18 Ⓐ Ⓑ Ⓒ Ⓓ Ⓔ
19 Ⓐ Ⓑ Ⓒ Ⓓ Ⓔ		19 Ⓐ Ⓑ Ⓒ Ⓓ Ⓔ	19 Ⓐ Ⓑ Ⓒ Ⓓ Ⓔ	19 Ⓐ Ⓑ Ⓒ Ⓓ Ⓔ
20 Ⓐ Ⓑ Ⓒ Ⓓ Ⓔ		20 Ⓐ Ⓑ Ⓒ Ⓓ Ⓔ	20 Ⓐ Ⓑ Ⓒ Ⓓ Ⓔ	20 Ⓐ Ⓑ Ⓒ Ⓓ Ⓔ
21 Ⓐ Ⓑ Ⓒ Ⓓ Ⓔ			21 Ⓐ Ⓑ Ⓒ Ⓓ Ⓔ	21 Ⓐ Ⓑ Ⓒ Ⓓ Ⓔ
22 Ⓐ Ⓑ Ⓒ Ⓓ Ⓔ			22 Ⓐ Ⓑ Ⓒ Ⓓ Ⓔ	22 Ⓐ Ⓑ Ⓒ Ⓓ Ⓔ
			23 Ⓐ Ⓑ Ⓒ Ⓓ Ⓔ	23 Ⓐ Ⓑ Ⓒ Ⓓ Ⓔ
			24 Ⓐ Ⓑ Ⓒ Ⓓ Ⓔ	

Check out our other COGAT® prep books for Kindergarten - Grade 5

www.GatewayGifted.com

Made in the USA
Las Vegas, NV
31 October 2024

10857646R10057